MORE 21ST CENTURY HITS

PART OF THE MUSIC SALES GROUP
LONDON / NEW YORK / PARIS / SYDNEY / COPENHAGEN / BERLIN / MADRID / TOKYO

8.95

ALSO AVAILABLE IN THE *REALLY EASY PIANO* SERIES...

ABBA
25 GREAT HITS. ORDER NO. AM980430

CHART HITS
21 BIG CHART HITS. ORDER NO. AM993377

CHRISTMAS
24 FESTIVE CHART HITS. ORDER NO. AM980496

CLASSICAL
36 POPULAR PIECES. ORDER NO. AM980419

CLASSICAL FAVOURITES
24 WELL-KNOWN FAVOURITES. ORDER NO. AM993366

COLDPLAY
20 SONGS FROM COLDPLAY. ORDER NO. AM989593

ELTON JOHN
24 CLASSIC SONGS. ORDER NO. AM987844

FRANK SINATRA
21 CLASSIC SONGS. ORDER NO. AM987833

GREAT FILM SONGS
22 BIG FILM HITS. ORDER NO. AM993344

GREAT SHOWSTOPPERS
20 POPULAR STAGE SONGS. ORDER NO. AM993355

JAZZ
24 JAZZ CLASSICS. ORDER NO. AM982773

LOVE SONGS
22 CLASSIC LOVE SONGS. ORDER NO. AM989582

NEW CHART HITS
19 BIG CHART HITS. ORDER NO. AM996523

NO. 1 HITS
22 POPULAR CLASSICS. ORDER NO. AM993388

POP HITS
22 GREAT SONGS. ORDER NO. AM980408

SHOWSTOPPERS
24 STAGE HITS. ORDER NO. AM982784

TV HITS
25 POPULAR HITS. ORDER NO. AM985435

60s HITS
25 CLASSIC HITS. ORDER NO. AM985402

70s HITS
25 CLASSIC SONGS. ORDER NO. AM985413

80s HITS
25 POPULAR HITS. ORDER NO. AM985424

90s HITS
24 POPULAR HITS. ORDER NO. AM987811

21ST CENTURY HITS
24 POPULAR HITS. ORDER NO. AM987822

50 FANTASTIC SONGS
FROM POP SONGS TO CLASSICAL THEMES. ORDER NO. AM997744

50 GREAT SONGS
FROM POP SONGS TO CLASSICAL THEMES. ORDER NO. AM995643

50 POPULAR SONGS
FROM POP SONGS TO CLASSICAL THEMES. ORDER NO. AM994400

PIANO TUTOR
FROM FIRST STEPS TO PLAYING IN A WIDE
RANGE OF STYLES — FAST!. ORDER NO. AM996303

ALL TITLES CONTAIN BACKGROUND NOTES FOR EACH SONG PLUS
PLAYING TIPS AND HINTS.

PUBLISHED BY
WISE PUBLICATIONS
14-15 BERNERS STREET, LONDON, W1T 3LJ, UK.

EXCLUSIVE DISTRIBUTORS:
MUSIC SALES LIMITED
DISTRIBUTION CENTRE, NEWMARKET ROAD, BURY ST EDMUNDS,
SUFFOLK, IP33 3YB, UK.
MUSIC SALES PTY LIMITED
20 RESOLUTION DRIVE, CARINGBAH, NSW 2229, AUSTRALIA.

ORDER NO. AM996534
ISBN 978-1-84772-935-4

MUSIC ARRANGED BY ZOE BOLTON.
MUSIC PROCESSED BY PAUL EWERS MUSIC DESIGN.
EDITED BY OLIVER MILLER.
PRINTED IN THE EU.

YOUR GUARANTEE OF QUALITY
AS PUBLISHERS, WE STRIVE TO PRODUCE EVERY BOOK TO THE HIGHEST COMMERCIAL STANDARDS. THE MUSIC HAS BEEN FRESHLY ENGRAVED AND THE BOOK HAS BEEN CAREFULLY DESIGNED TO MINIMISE AWKWARD PAGE TURNS AND TO MAKE PLAYING FROM IT A REAL PLEASURE.
PARTICULAR CARE HAS BEEN GIVEN TO SPECIFYING ACID-FREE, NEUTRAL-SIZED PAPER MADE FROM PULPS WHICH HAVE NOT BEEN ELEMENTAL CHLORINE BLEACHED. THIS PULP IS FROM FARMED SUSTAINABLE FORESTS AND WAS PRODUCED WITH SPECIAL REGARD FOR THE ENVIRONMENT.
THROUGHOUT, THE PRINTING AND BINDING HAVE BEEN PLANNED TO ENSURE A STURDY, ATTRACTIVE PUBLICATION WHICH SHOULD GIVE YEARS OF ENJOYMENT. IF YOUR COPY FAILS TO MEET OUR HIGH STANDARDS, PLEASE INFORM US AND WE WILL GLADLY REPLACE IT.

WWW.MUSICSALES.COM

U2

Beautiful Day

Words by Bono. Music by U2

The lead single from U2's album, *All That You Can't Leave Behind*, this optimistic anthem, about a man who has lost everything but nevertheless can find joy in what he still has, won three Grammy Awards in 2001 after becoming the veteran Irish rock band's fourth UK No. 1 single since their emergence in the early 1980s.

Hints & Tips: The left hand has a tricky part to play so work it out slowly and rhythmically, carefully placing the first beat of each bar. Keep it moving.

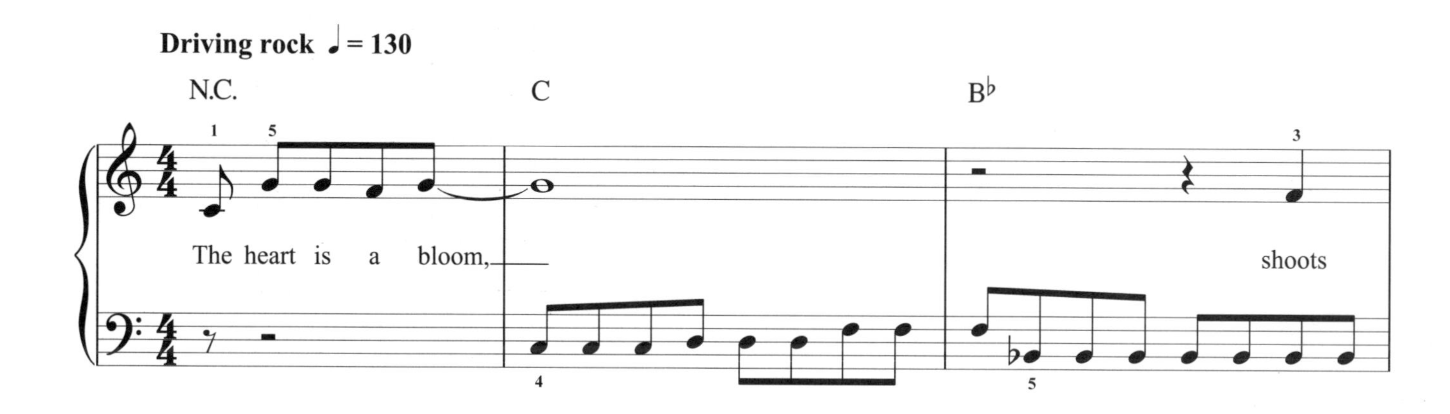

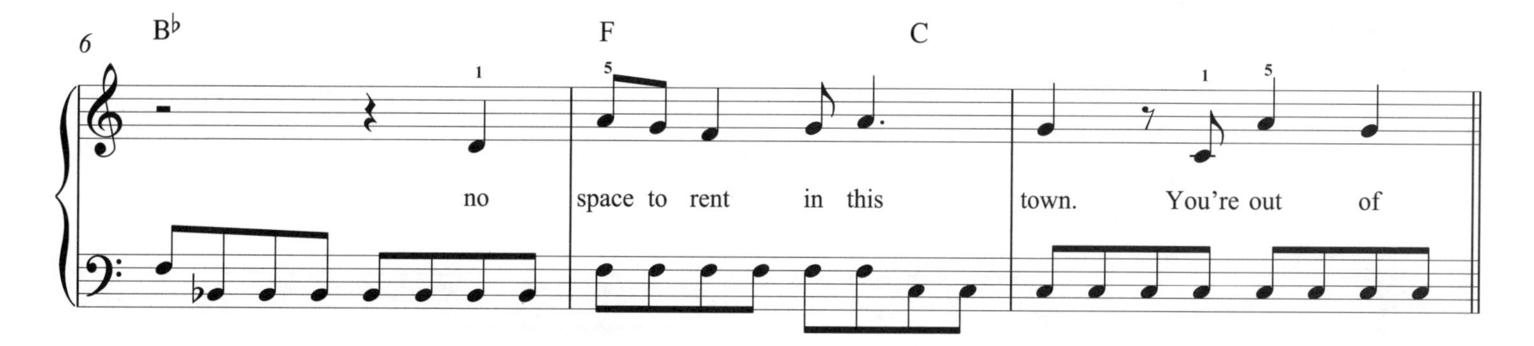

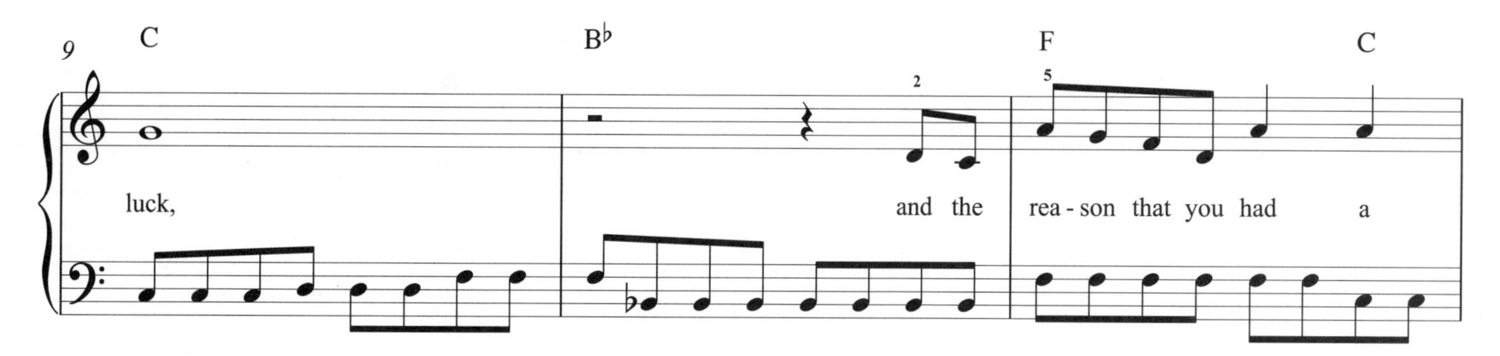

12
1 5
care, the traf - fic is stuck,

14
B♭ F C
1
and you're not mov - ing a - ny - where.

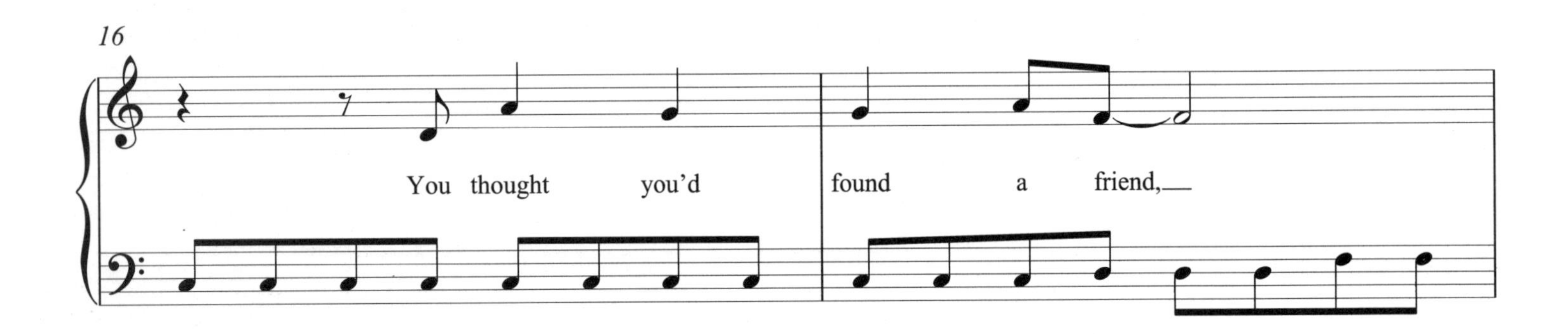
16
You thought you'd found a friend,

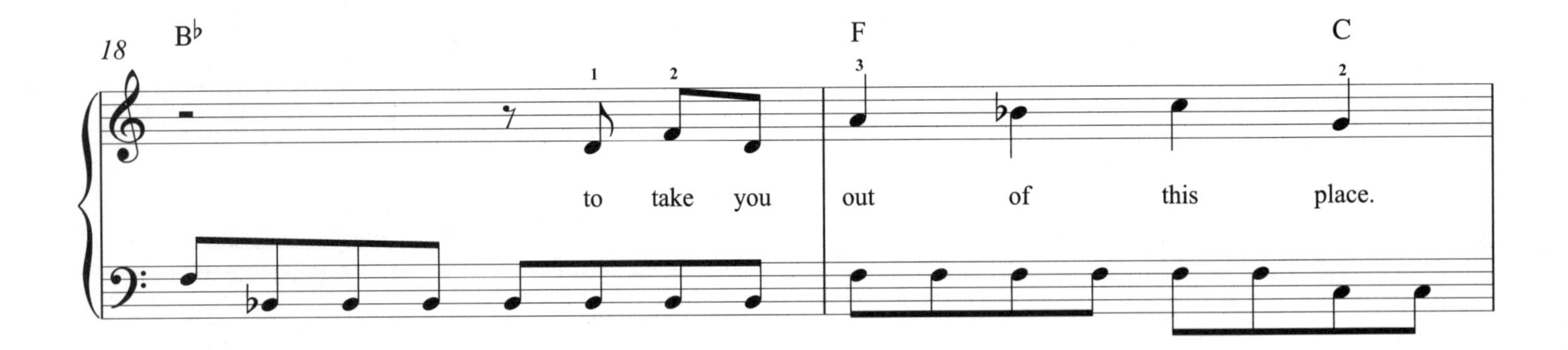
18
B♭ F C
1 2 3 2
to take you out of this place.

20
B♭
5
Some - one you could lend a hand in re -

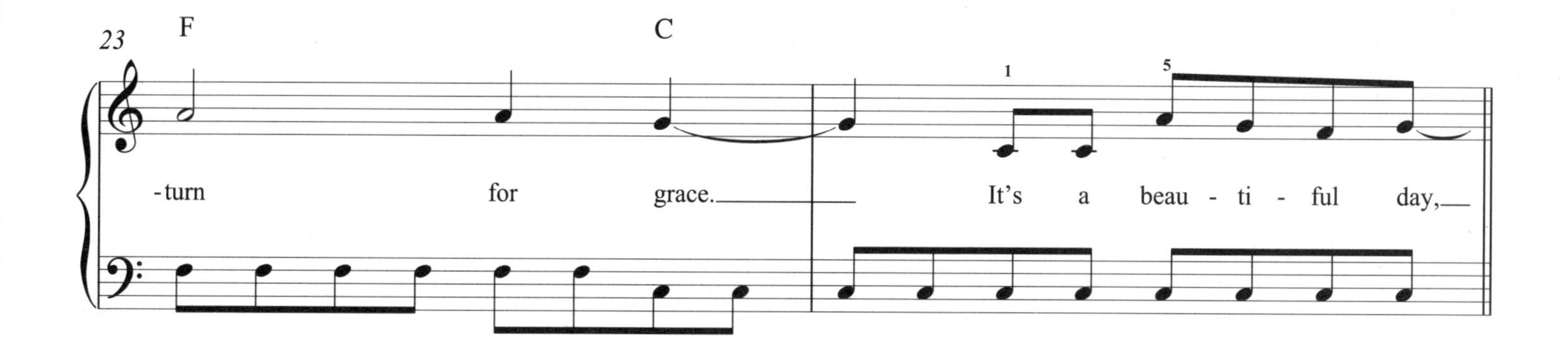
23
F
C
1
5
-turn for grace.
It's a beau - ti - ful day,

25
C
B♭
F
C
the sky falls and you feel

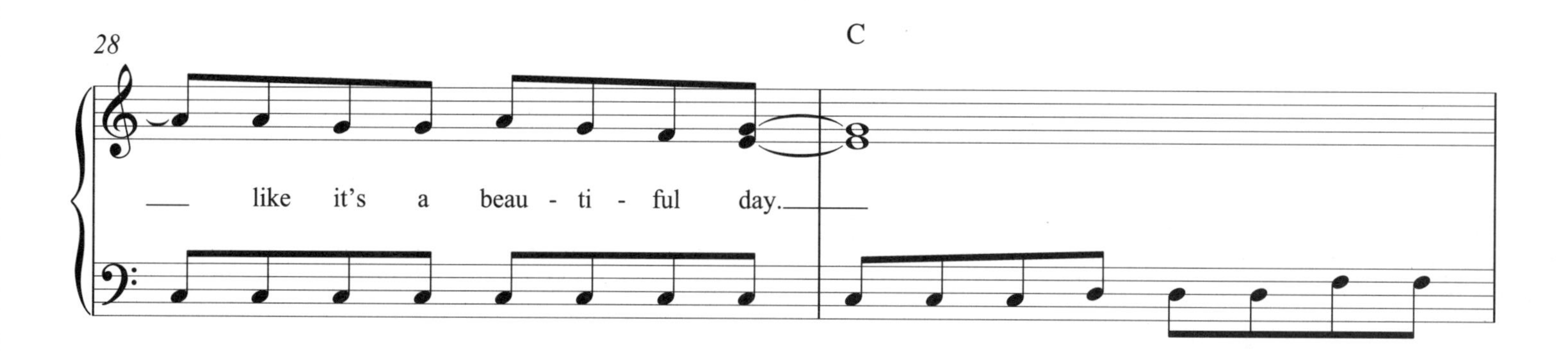
28
C
like it's a beau - ti - ful day.

30
B♭
F
C
The sky falls and you feel

32
Dm
B♭9
like it's a beau - ti - ful day.

McFly

All About You

Words & Music by Thomas Fletcher

McFly had their fifth hit in less than a year when this song, released as a double A-side along with their version of Carole King's classic, 'You've Got A Friend', became their third UK No. 1 in March 2005. It was that year's official Comic Relief single and was also used to promote the charity Make Poverty History.

Hints & Tips: Although a simple bass-line for the left hand it still needs to be played accurately. At bar 32 try not to rush the triplet, keep it even.

17
C E7/B Am Am/G
Then you whis - pered in my ear and you told me too, said you'd
21
F G C
make my life worth - while, it's all a - bout you. And
25
F Fm C G/B Am
I would ans - wer all your wish - es if you asked me to. But if
29
D7 G
you de - ny me one of your kiss - es, don't know what I'd do. Oh,
33
C E/B Am
so hold me close and say three words like you used to
36
Am/G F G C
do. Danc - ing on the kit - chen tiles, it's all a - bout you.

David Gray

Babylon

Words & Music by David Gray

This was the first of seven UK hits for the Manchester-born singer/songwriter between 2000 and 2003. Its popularity, particularly with radio listeners, led to his album *White Ladder*, from which it was taken, reaching No. 1 in the UK charts in 2001 after 64 weeks in the Top 40, two years and five months after its release.

Hints & Tips: This is a good song for practising the spacing of two notes in one hand, therefore playing the suggested fingerings is advised.

12
B♭7
F7
B♭7
to
op - en up my heart to all that
jea - lous - y, that bit - ter - ness, that

15
F7
F
C
ri - di - cule.
An' if you want it
come an' get it,

19
Gm
Am
F
C
for cry - in' out loud.
The love that I was
giv - in' you was

23
Gm
B♭
F
C
nev - er in
doubt.
Let go your heart,
let go your head,

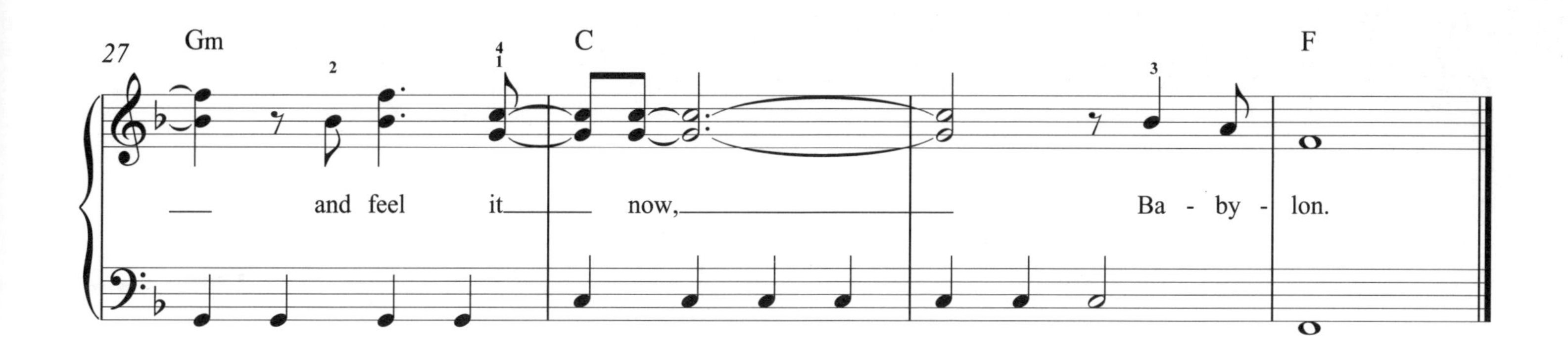
27
Gm
C
F
and feel
it
now,
Ba - by - lon.

SNOW PATROL

Chasing Cars

Words & Music by Gary Lightbody, Nathan Connolly, Jonathan Quinn, Paul Wilson & Tom Simpson

The longevity of this CD single in the UK charts illustrates the impact of legal downloads because, although it peaked at No. 6, it has spent at least 130 weeks in the Top 100 despite a physical copy being available for only 14 of them. Its popularity in the US came after it featured on the TV medical drama *Grey's Anatomy*.

Hints & Tips: Keep the left hand legato (smooth) throughout. The constant left-hand quaver rhythm should make the right-hand part easier to count but be accurate with the syncopation.

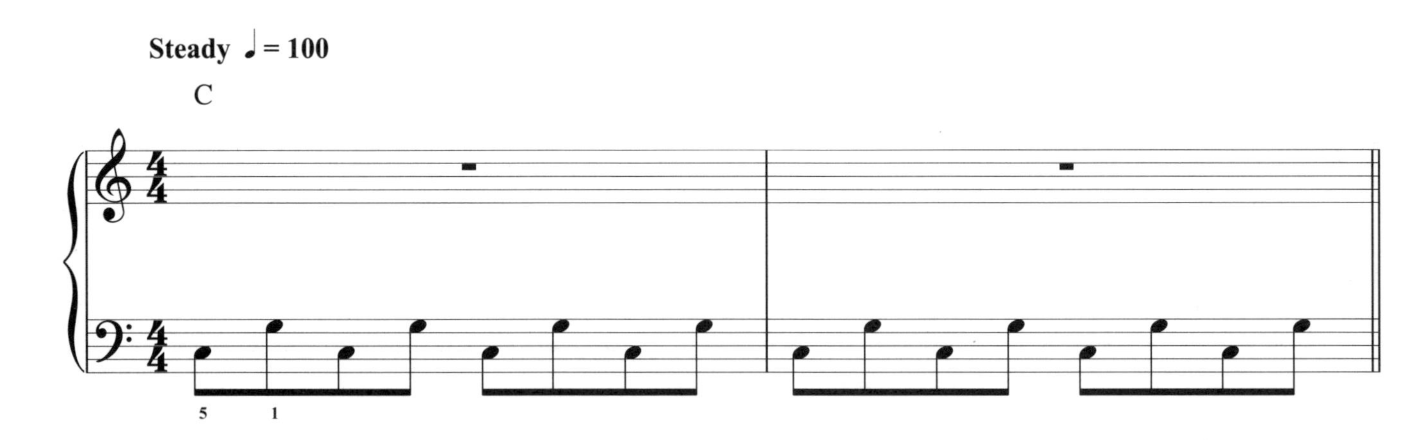

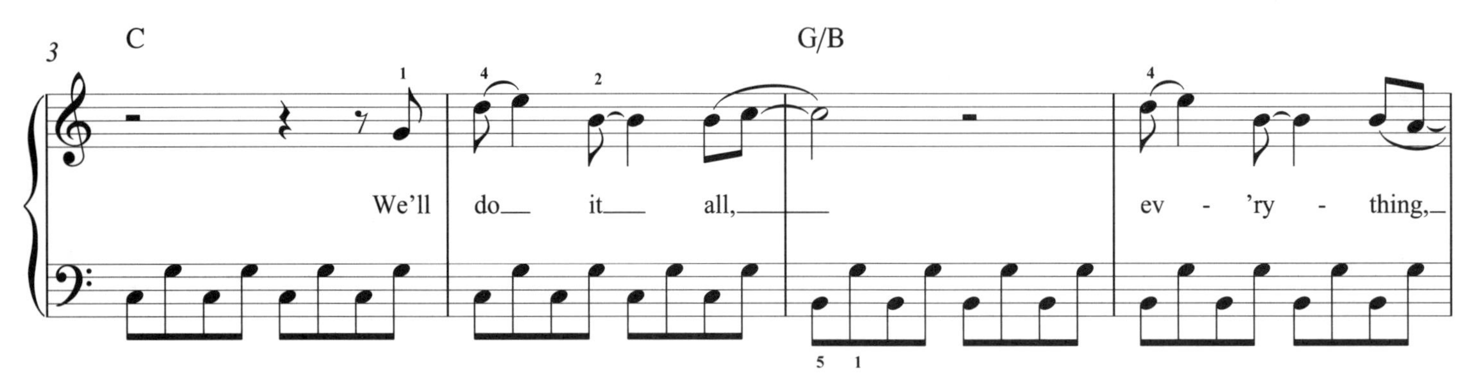

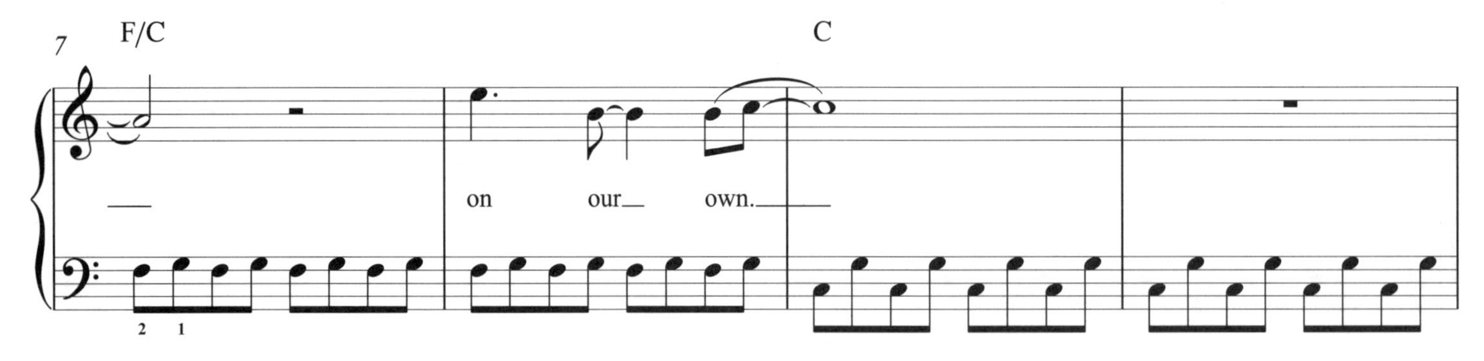

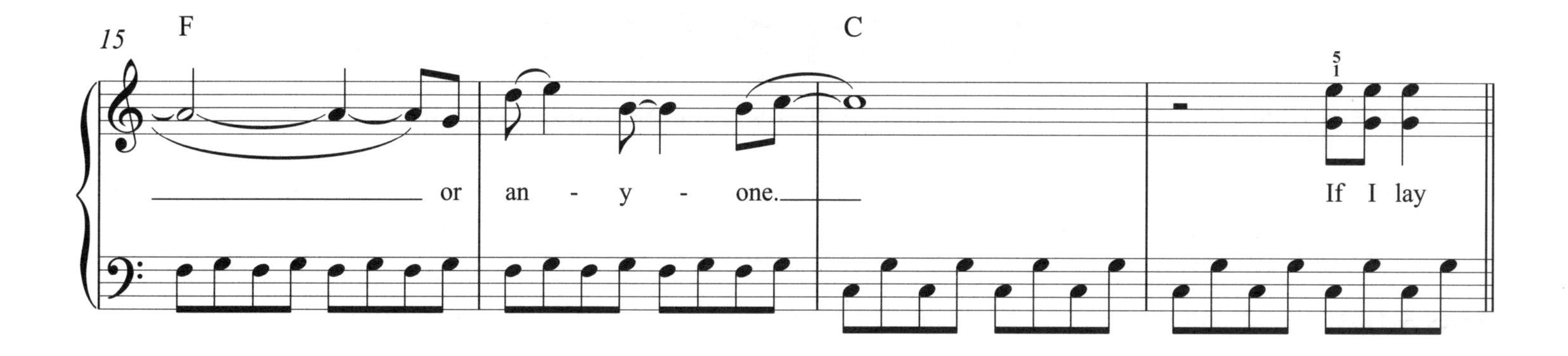
15
F
C
or an - y - one.
If I lay

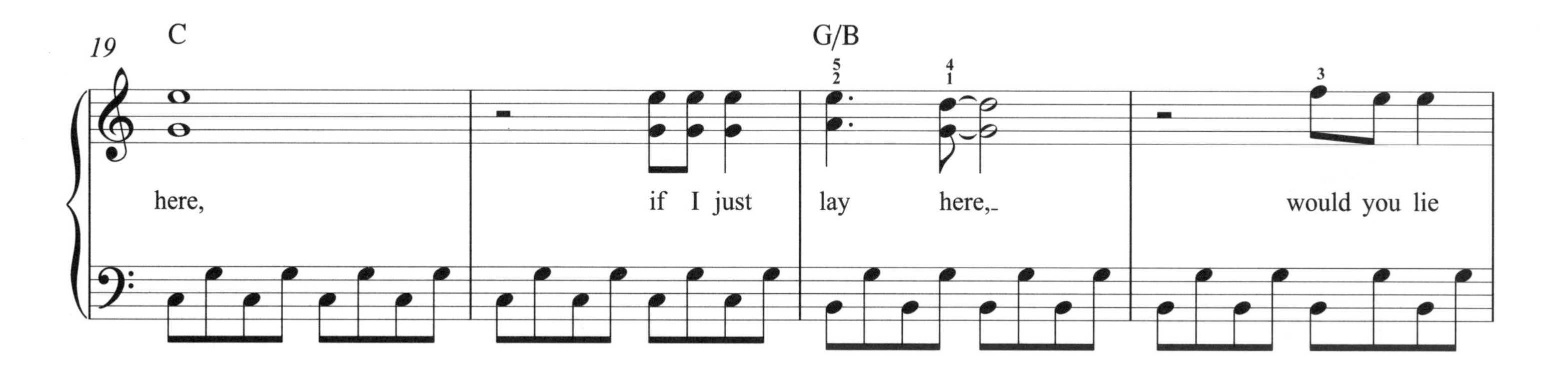
19
C
G/B
here,
if I just
lay here,
would you lie

23
F
C
with me and
just for - get the world.

26
G/B
For-get what we're
told,
be-fore we get
too old.

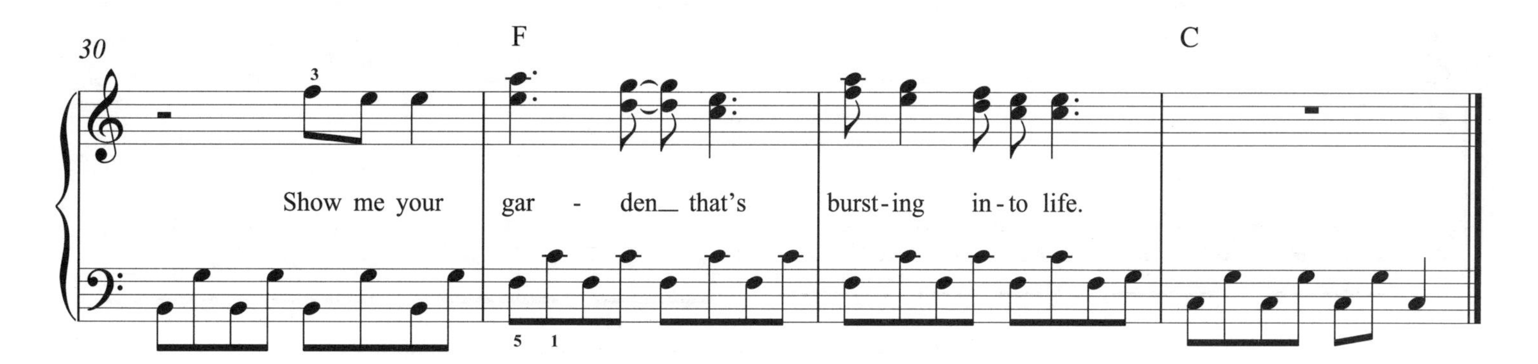
30
F
C
Show me your
gar - den that's
burst-ing in-to life.

Newton Faulkner

Dream Catch Me

Words & Music by Crispin Hunt, Gordon Mills & Newton Faulkner

This song's huge UK chart success came after it was selected as Jo Whiley's Pet Sound on her daily Radio1 show in June 2007. Its exposure led to Newton Faulkner's debut album, *Hand Built By Robots*, from which it was the second single, topping the UK album charts for four weeks later the same year.

Hints & Tips: Keep the left hand smooth and rhythmic throughout and take care of the syncopation in the right-hand part.

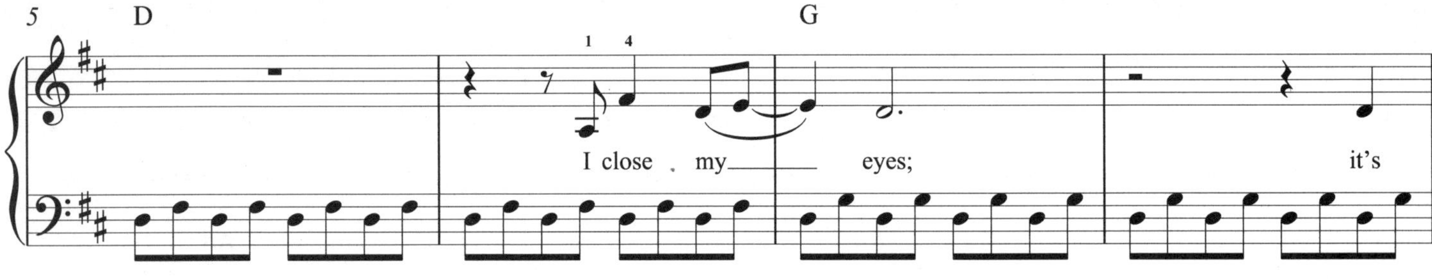

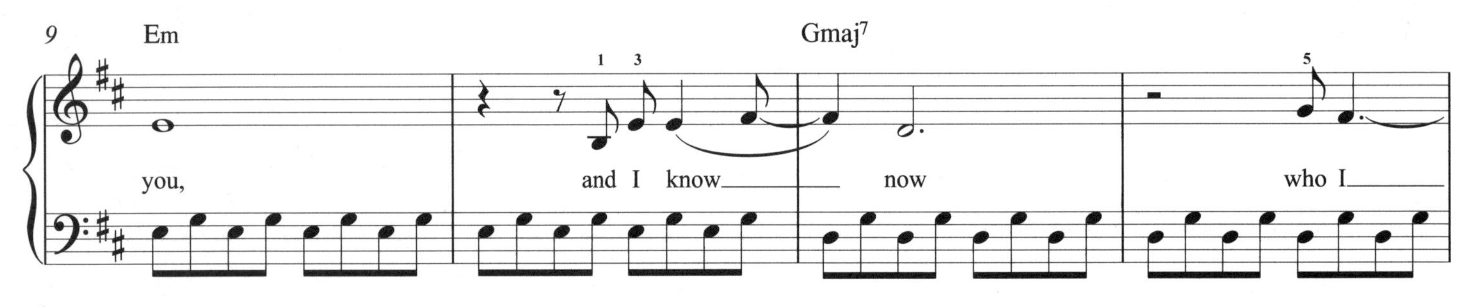

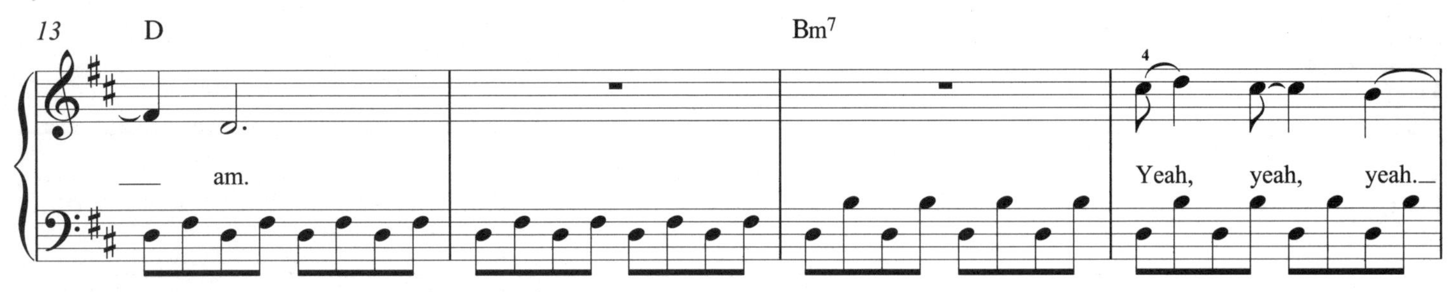

21
Dadd9
A/C♯
There's a place I go
when I'm a - lone,
do an-y-thing I want,

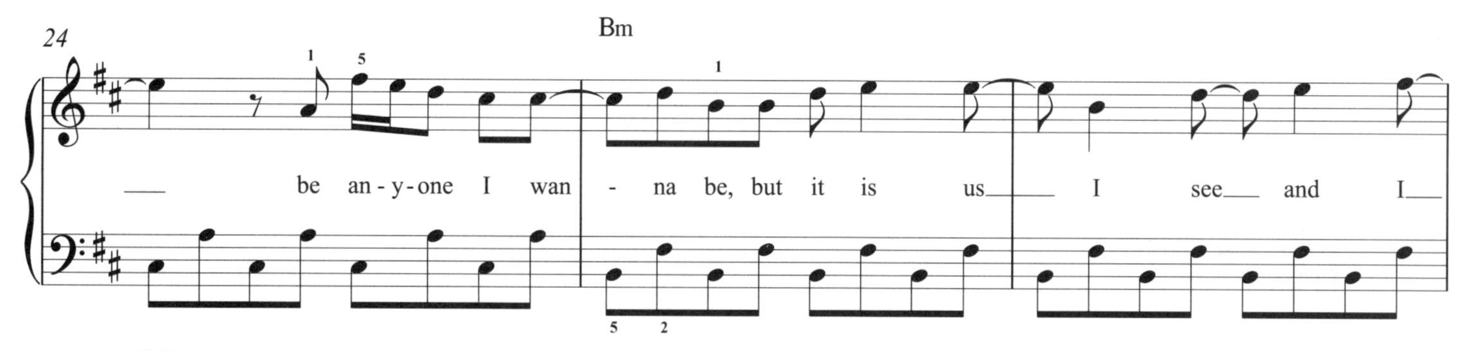
24
Bm
be an-y-one I wan - na be, but it is us
I see and I

27
G/D
D
can - not be - lieve I'm fall - in'.
That's where I'm go - in',

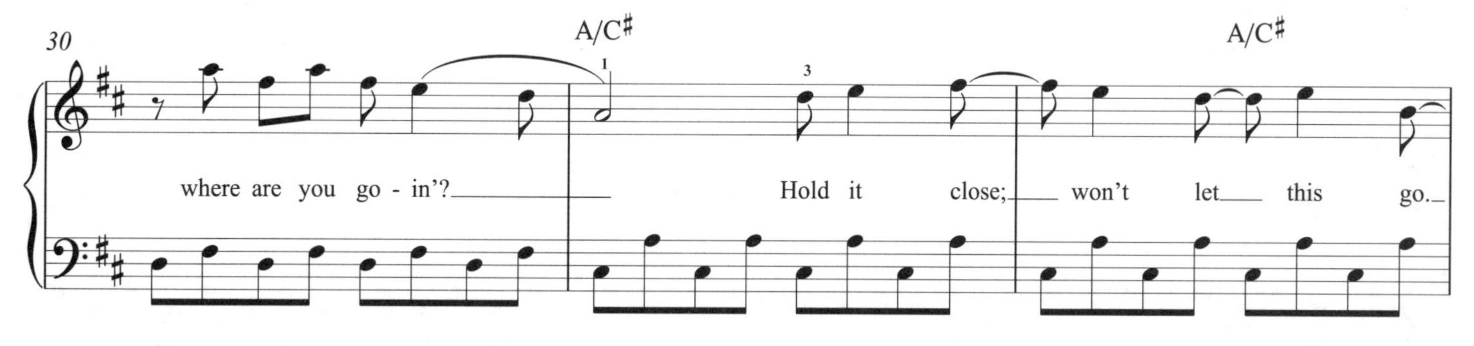
30
A/C♯
A/C♯
where are you go - in'?
Hold it close; won't let this go.

33
Bm
G
Dream catch me,
yeah.
Dream catch

36
Em
G
D
me when I fall,
or else I won't come back at all.

Britney Spears

Everytime

Words & Music by Britney Spears & Annette Stamatelatos

Having had much negative publicity, in 2004 Britney Spears quickly consolidated her resurgence when, in June, this tragic ballad, believed to be about former boyfriend Justin Timberlake, became her fifth single to top the charts, soon after the similar success, in March, of 'Toxic', her first hit after a gap of nearly four years.

Hints & Tips: This is a gentle song (the original contains a harp, the softest of instruments), so treat it as such; play softly.

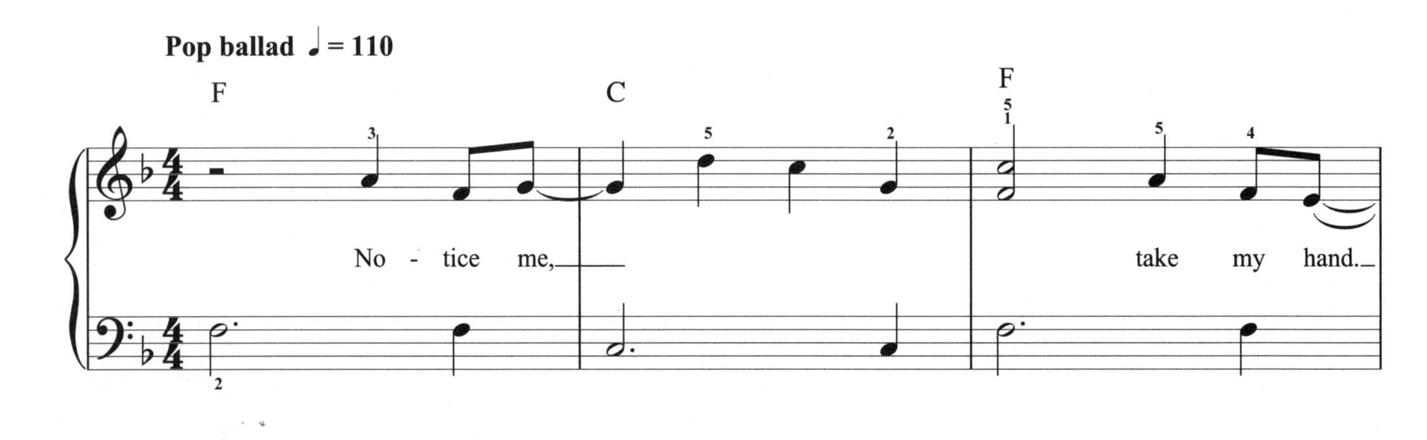

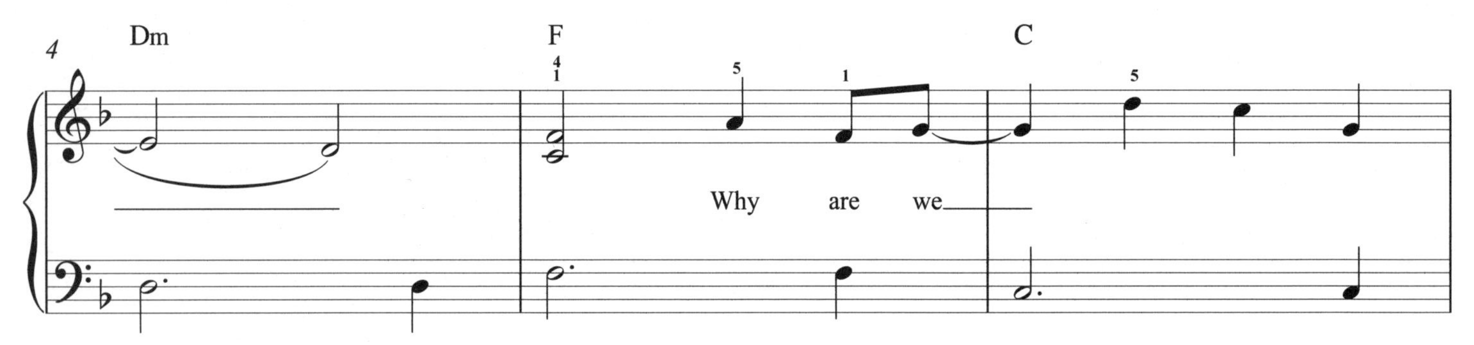

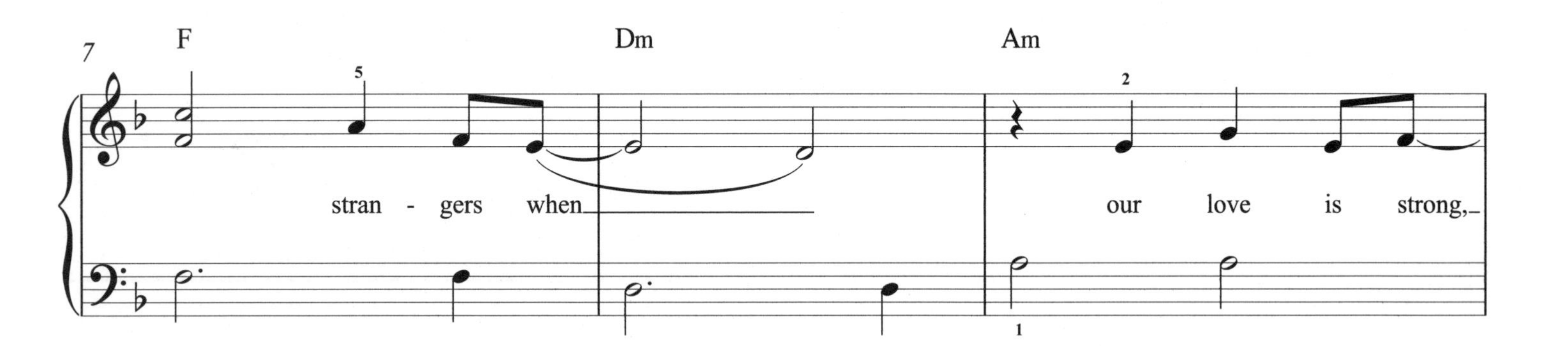

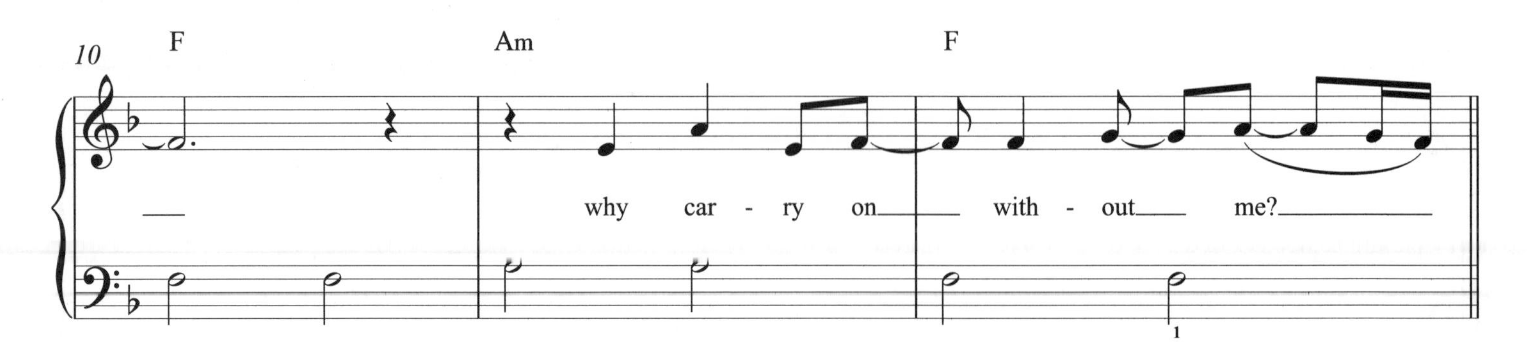

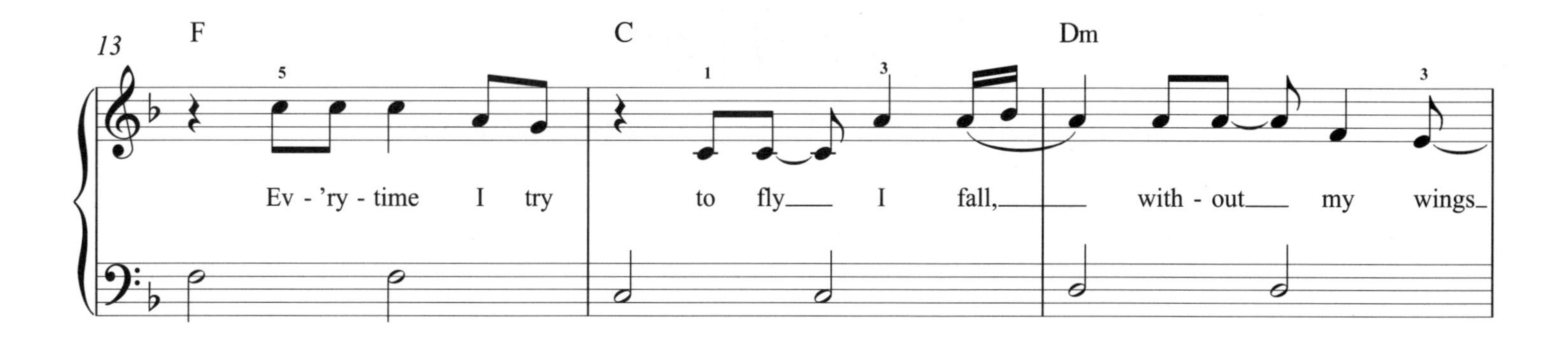
13
F
C
Dm
Ev - 'ry - time I try
to fly I fall,
with - out my wings

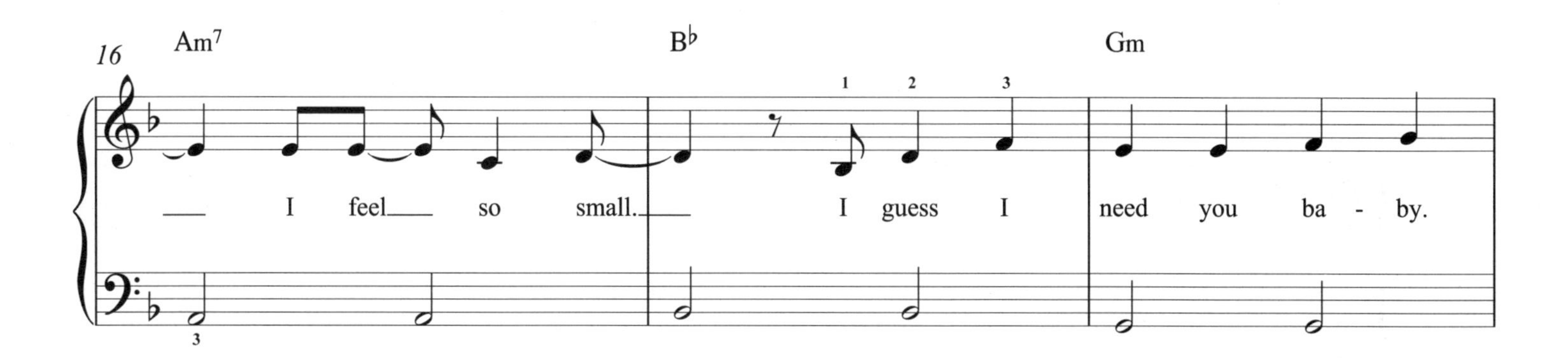
16
Am7
B♭
Gm
I feel so small.
I guess I
need you ba - by.

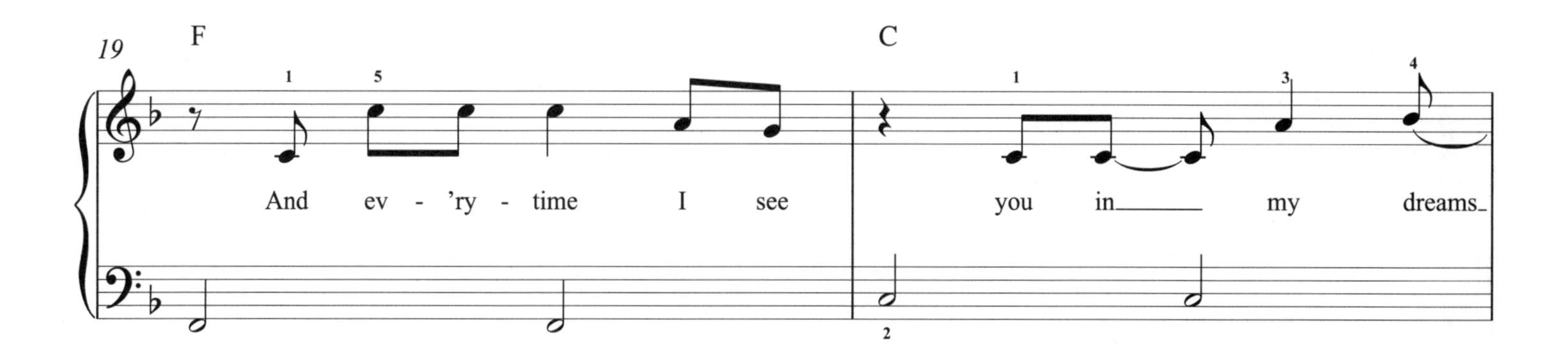
19
F
C
And ev - 'ry - time I see
you in my dreams

21
Dm
Am7
B♭
I see your face,
it's haunt - ing me.
I guess I

24
Gm
F
need you ba - by.

COLDPLAY

Fix You

Words & Music by Guy Berryman, Chris Martin, Jon Buckland & Will Champion

When released as an EP on iTunes Music Store in September 2005 all sales went to the American Red Cross Hurricane 2005 Relief and the National Academy of Recording Arts & Sciences' MusiCare Hurricane Relief Fund. It became a tribute song for victims of the disaster, although it is also said to have been written by Chris Martin for his wife Gwyneth Paltrow, to comfort her after the death of her father.

Hints & Tips: Practise the right-hand part in the chorus, paying particular attention to the recommended fingering and trying to move between the notes as smoothly as possible.

10
Dm C F Am Dm C
when you lose some-thing you can't re - place,
when you

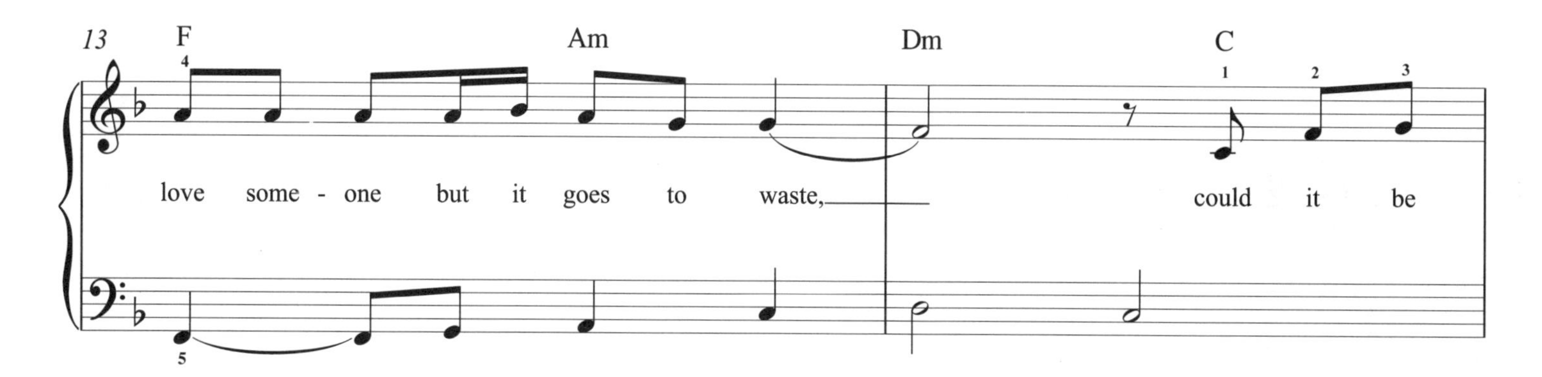
13
F Am Dm C
love some - one but it goes to waste,
could it be

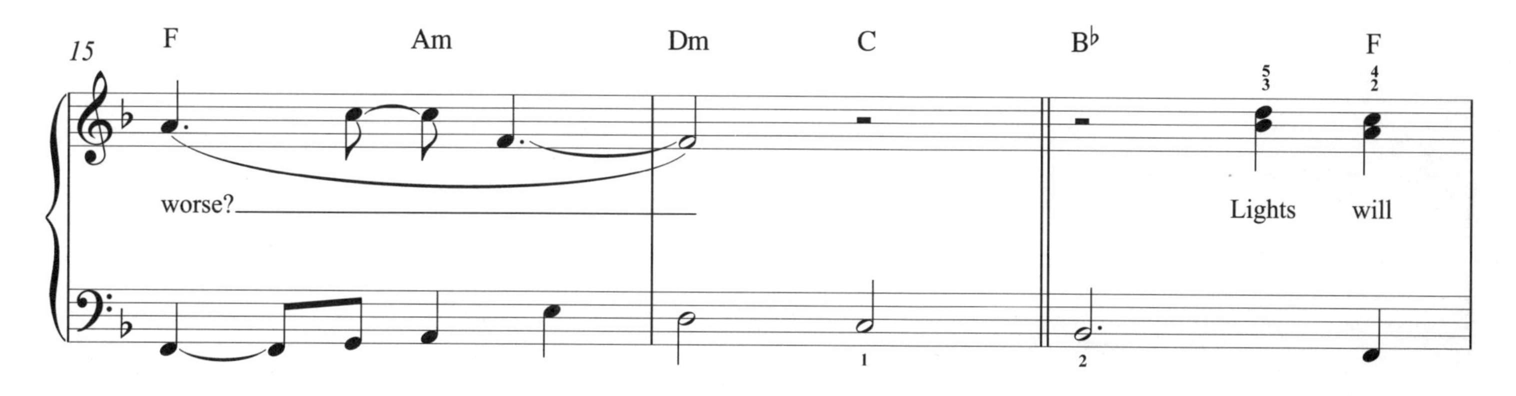
15
F Am Dm C B♭ F
worse?
Lights will

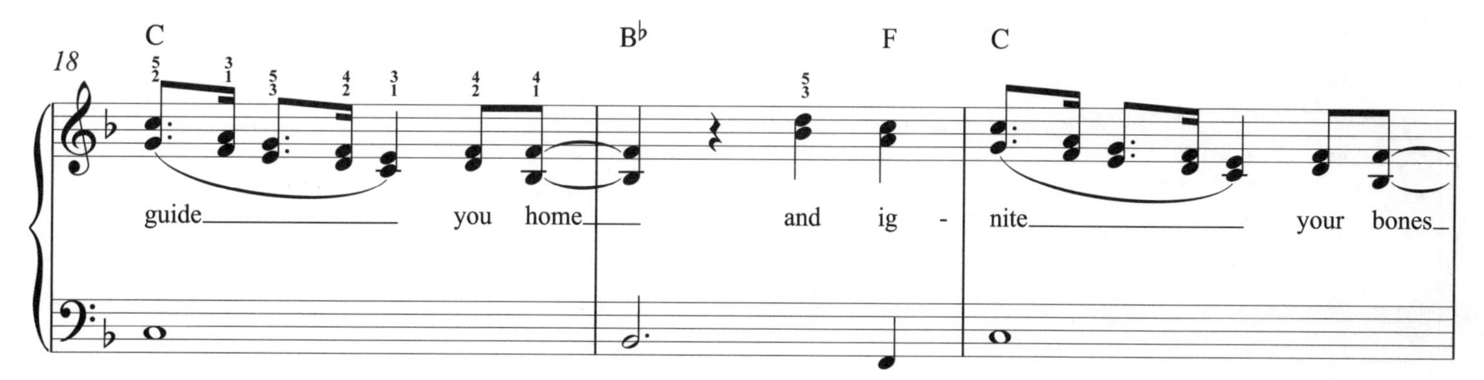
18
C B♭ F C
guide you home and ig - nite your bones

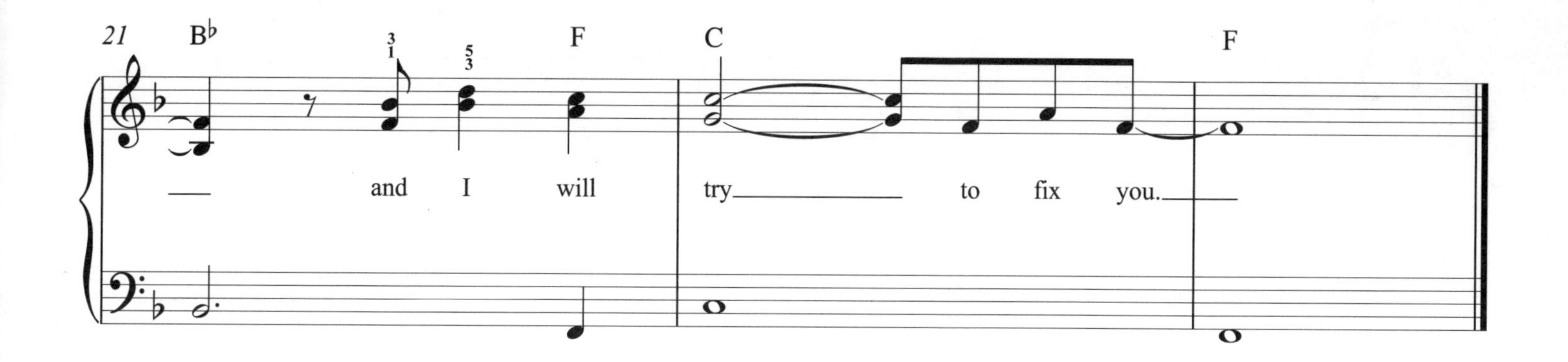
21
B♭ F C F
and I will try to fix you.

MIKA

Grace Kelly

Words & Music by Michael Penniman, Jodi Marr, Dan Warner & John Merchant

Meant as a mocking satire of musicians who reinvent themselves in order to be popular, this song by Beirut-born Mika, which includes references to Rossini's opera *The Barber of Seville*, became only the second to reach No. 1 on downloads alone when it topped the UK charts for five weeks from late January 2007 onwards.

Hints & Tips: The first thing to notice about this song is the swing rhythm, so all quavers are divided as indicated after the metronome marking. Secondly, there are many groups of triplets, so take care that they are played rhythmically and even.

13
G
Dm7
Am7
So I try a lit - tle
Fred - die.
I've gone i - den - ti - ty

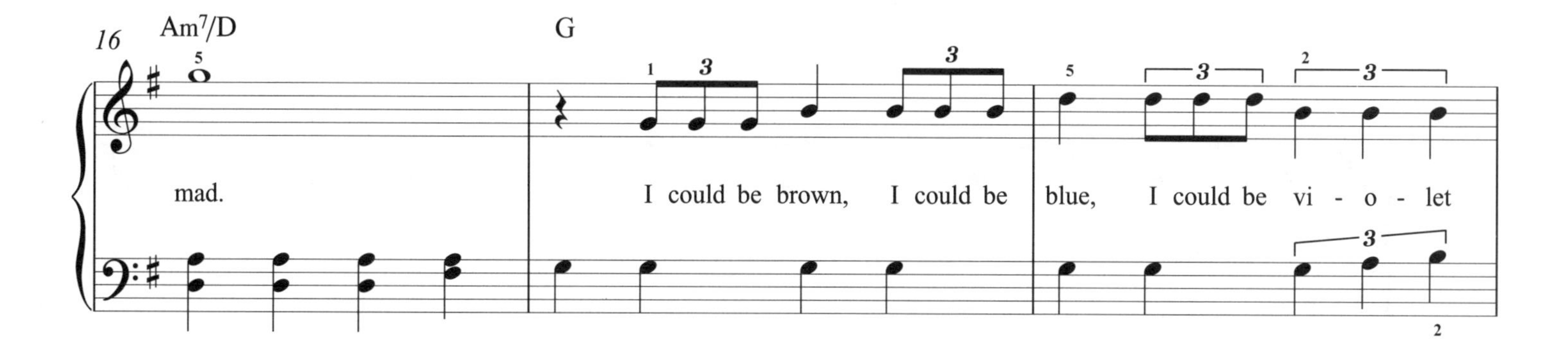
16
Am7/D
G
mad.
I could be brown, I could be
blue, I could be vi - o - let

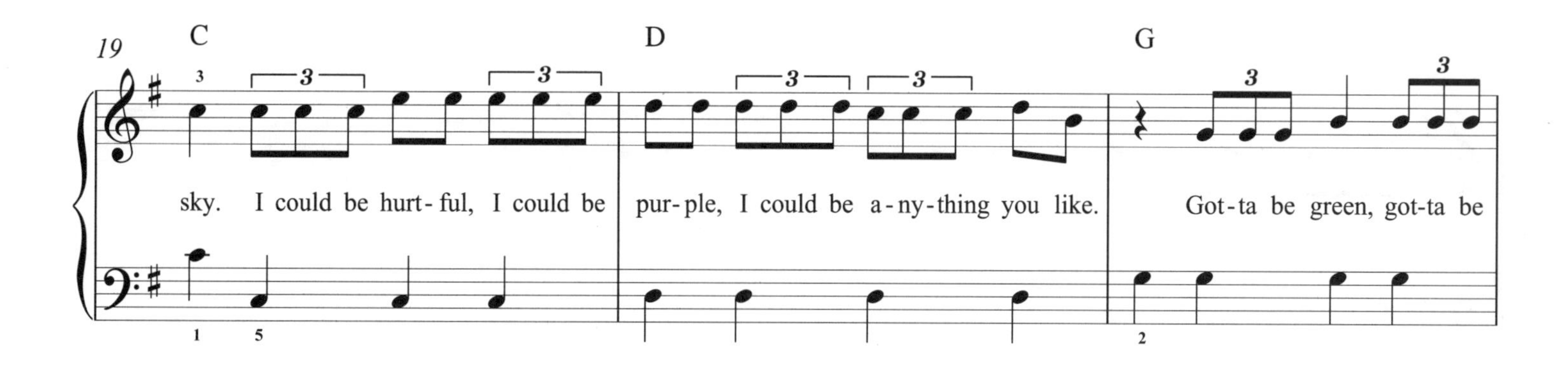
19
C
D
G
sky. I could be hurt- ful, I could be
pur- ple, I could be a - ny - thing you like.
Got - ta be green, got - ta be

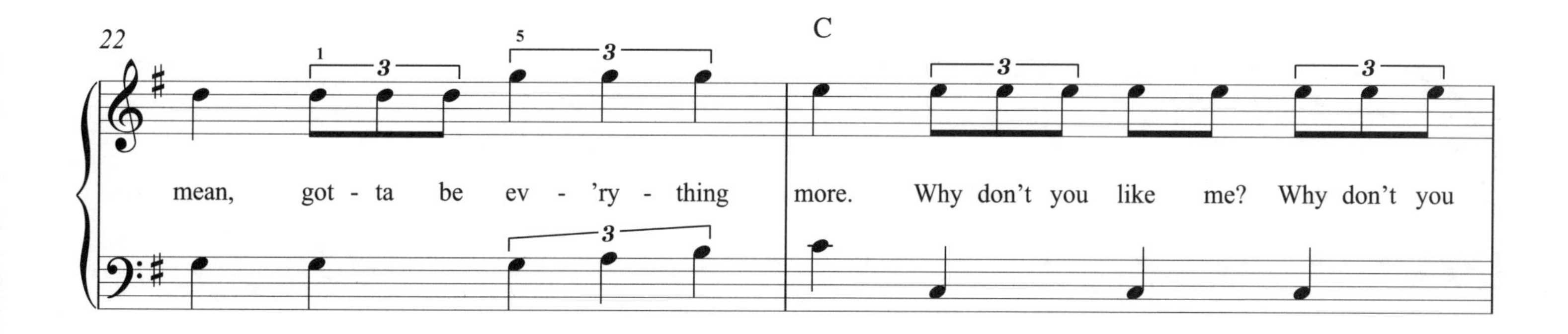
22
C
mean, got - ta be ev - 'ry - thing
more. Why don't you like me? Why don't you

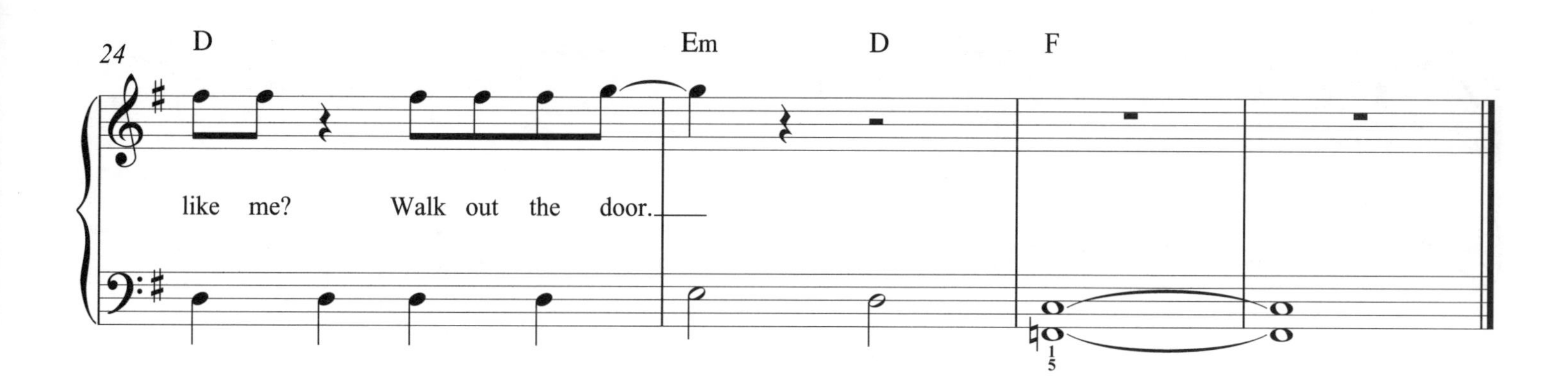
24
D
Em
D
F
like me? Walk out the door.

Hero

Words & Music by Enrique Iglesias, Paul Barry & Mark Taylor

Having had a hit in 1981 with 'Begin The Beguine', Julio Iglesias and Enrique became the first father and son to top the UK charts as solo artists when this song went straight to No. 1 after its release here in 2002. It had already been critically acclaimed in the US in 2001 after the 9/11 attacks on the World Trade Centre.

Hints & Tips: Quite a complex rhythm with the left-hand syncopated rhythm makes this a tricky piece requiring slow practice, preferably with a metronome.

12
D/A
G
Em7
this. Now would you
die, for the one you
love? Hold me

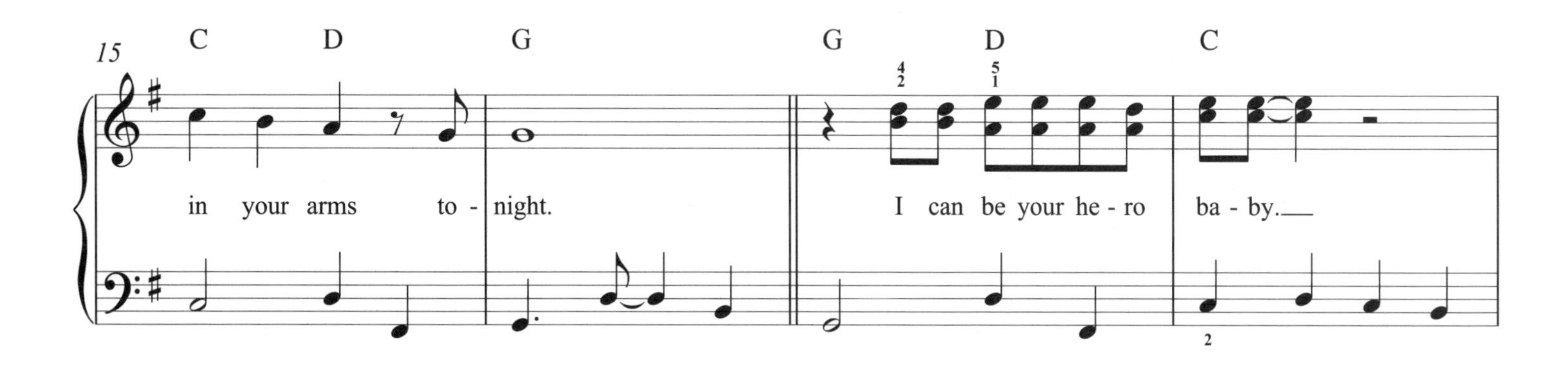
15
C D G
G D C
in your arms to - night.
I can be your he - ro
ba - by.

19
G D C G D C
I can kiss a - way your pain.
I will stand by you for ev - er.

23
G D/F♯ C G D/F♯
You can take my breath a - way.
You can take my

26
C G D7/F♯ C
breath a - way.
I can be your he - ro.

CHRISTINA AGUILERA

Hurt

Words & Music by Linda Perry, Christina Aguilera & Mark Ronson

A huge hit across Europe in late 2006, this power ballad, acclaimed for its lyrics about how one deals with the loss of a loved one, was the second single from Aguilera's album, *Back To Basics*, which she describes as a throwback to the 20s, 30s, and 40s-style jazz, blues and feel-good soul music, but with a modern twist.

Hints & Tips: Although the left-hand part is quite simple, try not to get lazy or sloppy with the rhythm.

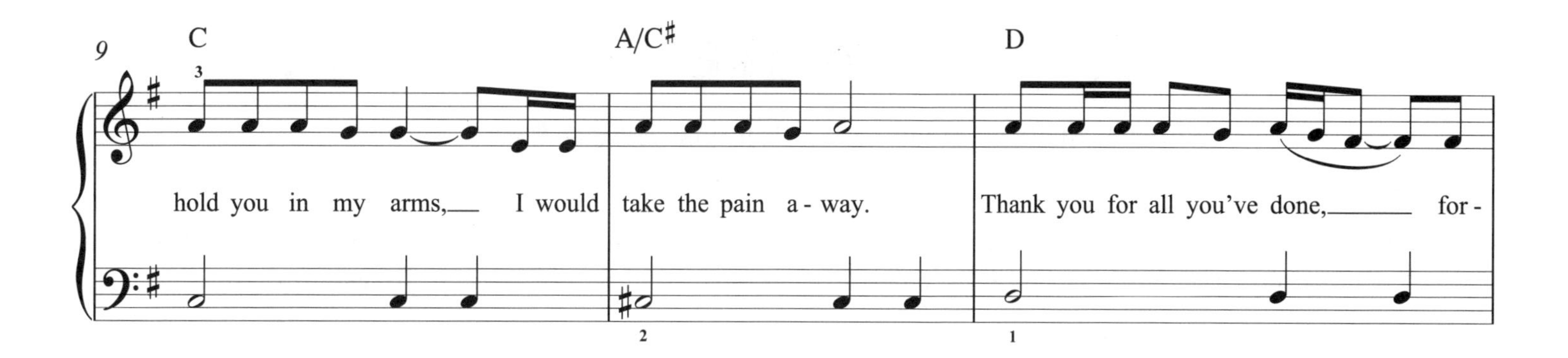
9
C
A/C♯
D
hold you in my arms, I would take the pain a-way. Thank you for all you've done, for-

12
B/D♯
C
A/C♯
-give all your mis-takes. There's no-thing I would-n't do to hear your voice a-gain. Some-

15
D
B/D♯
Em
-times I want to call you, but I know you won't be there. Woah, I'm sor-ry for

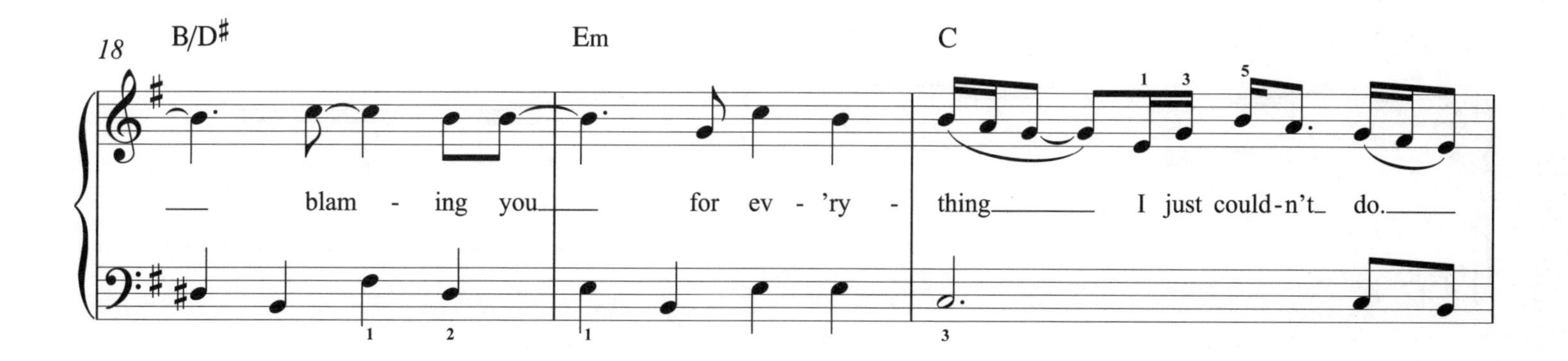
18
B/D♯
Em
C
blam-ing you for ev-'ry-thing I just could-n't do.

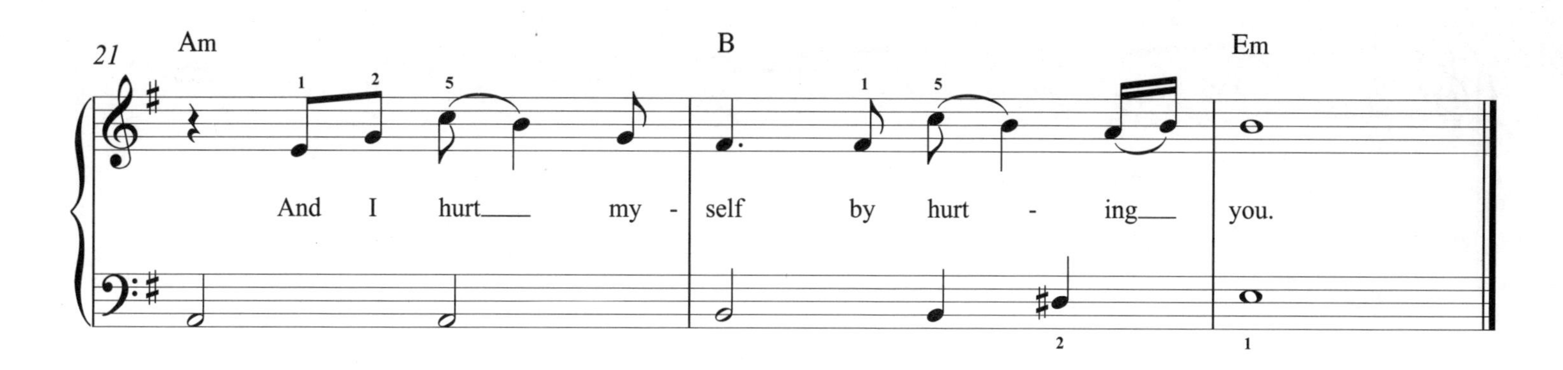
21
Am
B
Em
And I hurt my-self by hurt-ing you.

Ronan Keating

If Tomorrow Never Comes

Words & Music by Garth Brooks & Kent Blazy

Originally a 1989 hit for American country music artist Garth Brooks, this has subsequently become his signature song and one of his most popular songs for other artists to perform. Ronan Keating recorded his version in 2001 for the album *Destination* and in May 2002 it went on to become his third UK No. 1 single.

Hints & Tips: Playing the suggested fingerings in this song would be advisable; there is a lot of movement for the left hand and bars 20–21 are tricky for the right hand, requiring slow, hands separate practice.

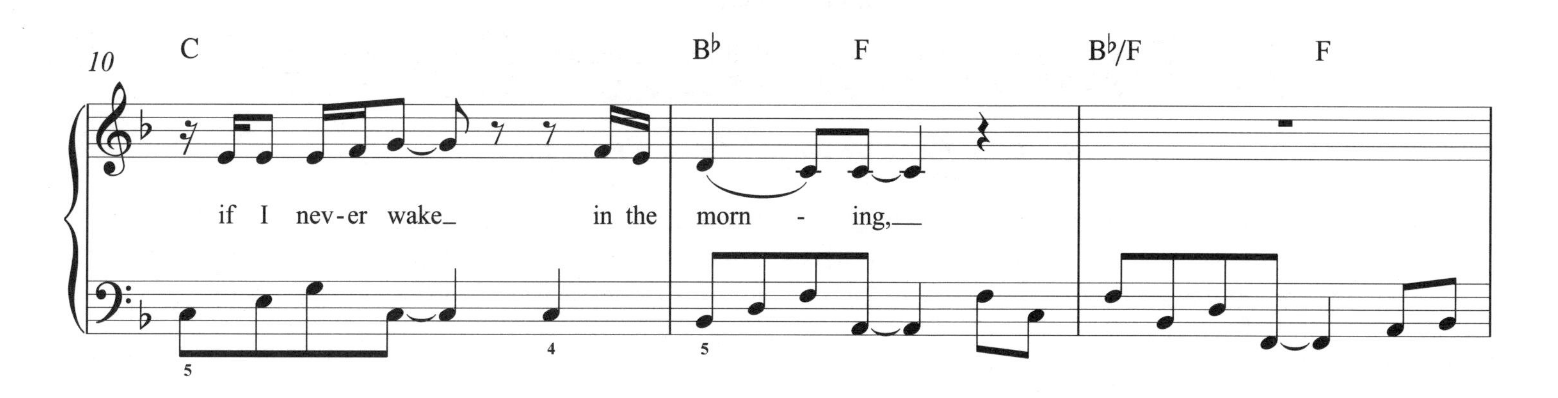
10
C
B♭
F
B♭/F
F
if I nev-er wake_ in the morn - ing,_

13
C
Gm
C
B♭
F
B♭
would she ev-er doubt, the way I feel a-bout her in my heart._

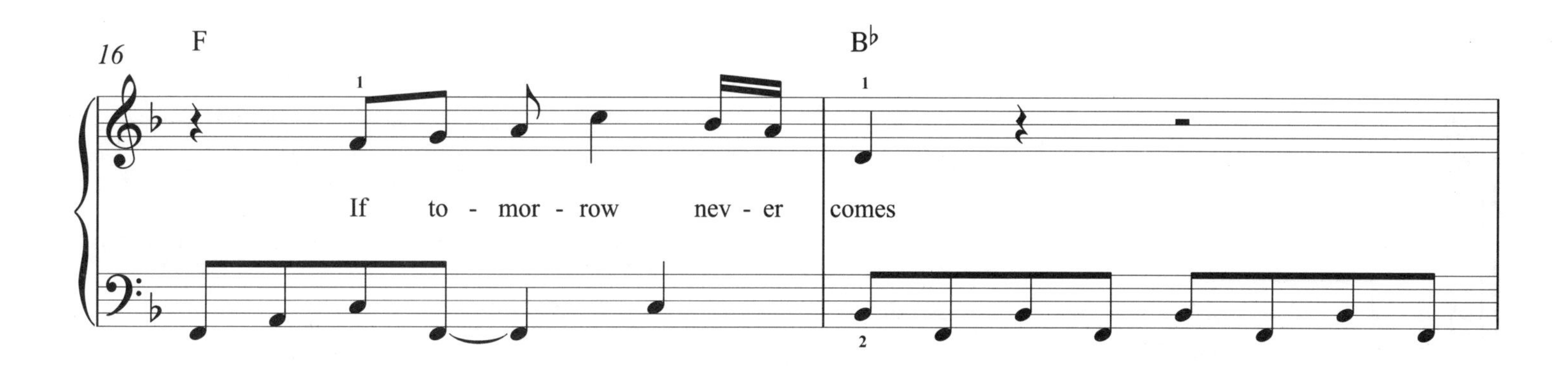
16
F
B♭
If to - mor - row nev - er comes

18
F
will she know how much I love her?_

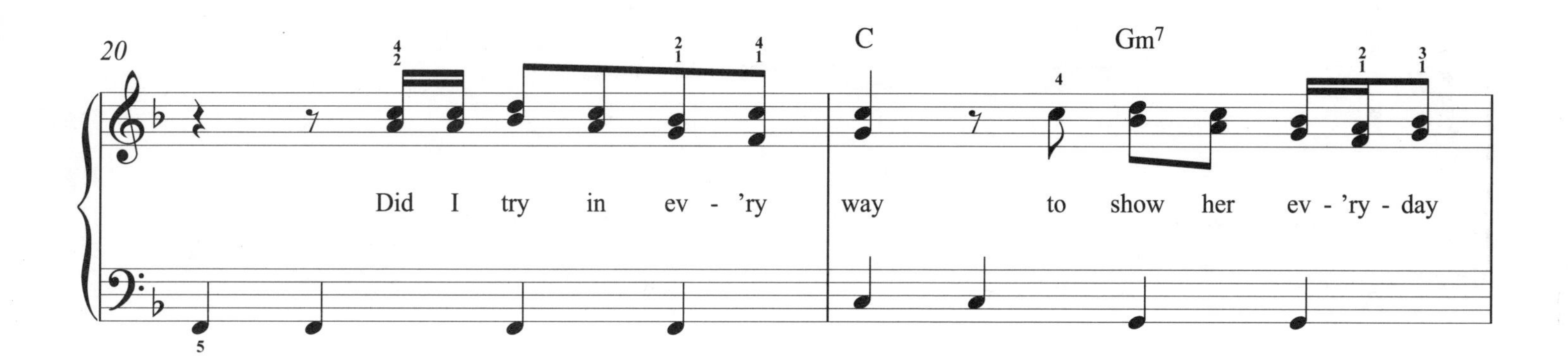
20
C
Gm7
Did I try in ev - 'ry way to show her ev - 'ry - day

22
C
B♭
F
she's my on - ly
one?

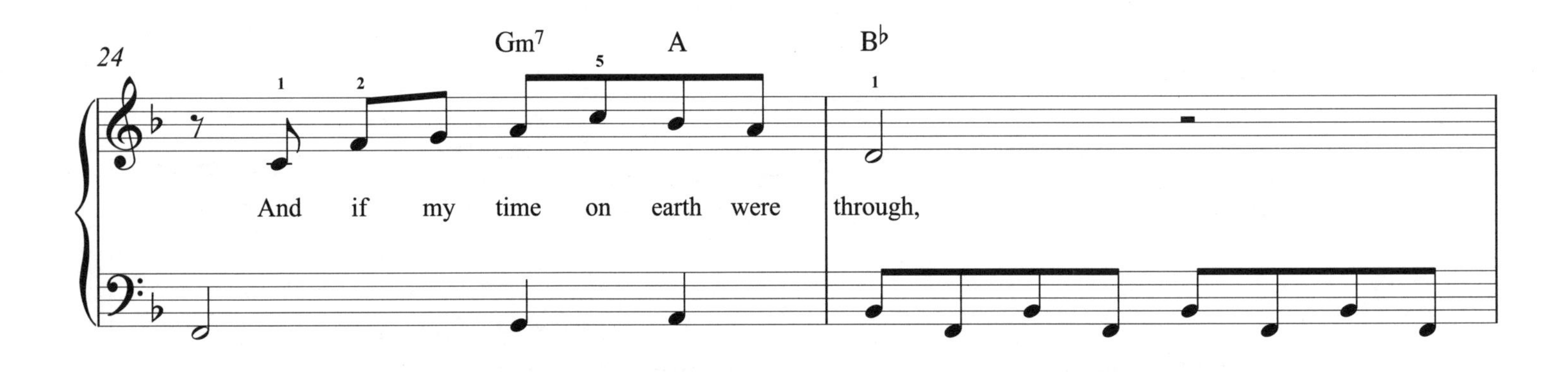
24
Gm7
A
B♭
And if my time on earth were
through,

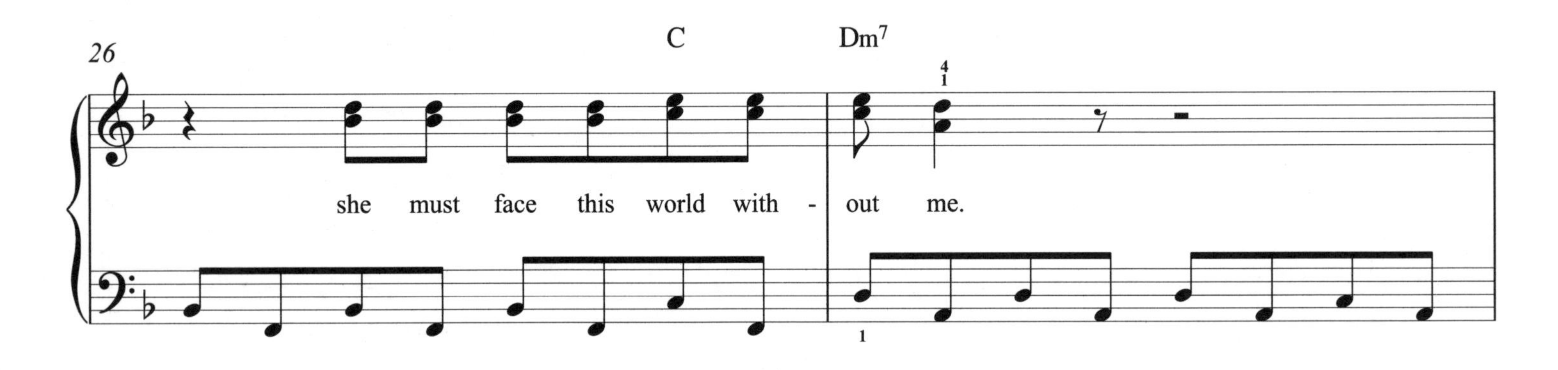
26
C
Dm7
she must face this world with -
out me.

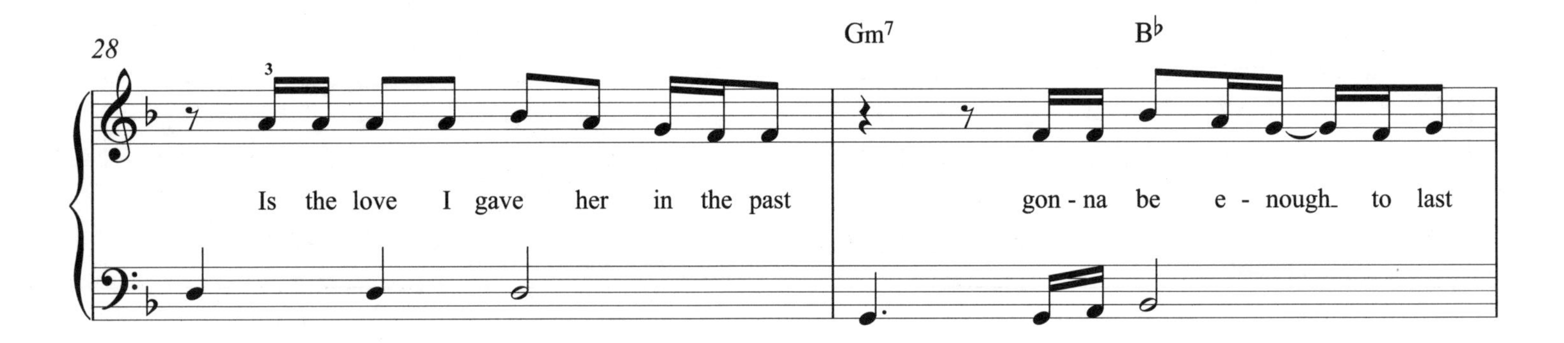
28
Gm7
B♭
Is the love I gave her in the past
gon - na be e - nough to last

30
C
F
C
B♭
F
if to mo row never
comes?

A Thousand Miles

Words & Music by Vanessa Carlton

Vanessa Carlton describes this song, recorded for her debut album *Be Not Nobody*, as "a combination of reality and fantasy. It's about a love that so consumes you that you'd do anything for it". Written about someone whom she had a crush on, she has admitted that he remained unaware of her unreciprocated feelings for him.

Hints & Tips: The syncopated rhythm is the trickiest thing in this song. Set a metronome to beat the quaver pulse and practise it slowly. Many of the motifs are repeated, for example, once you have mastered bars 1–4 you will also be able to play bars 7–8, 11–12 and 25–28.

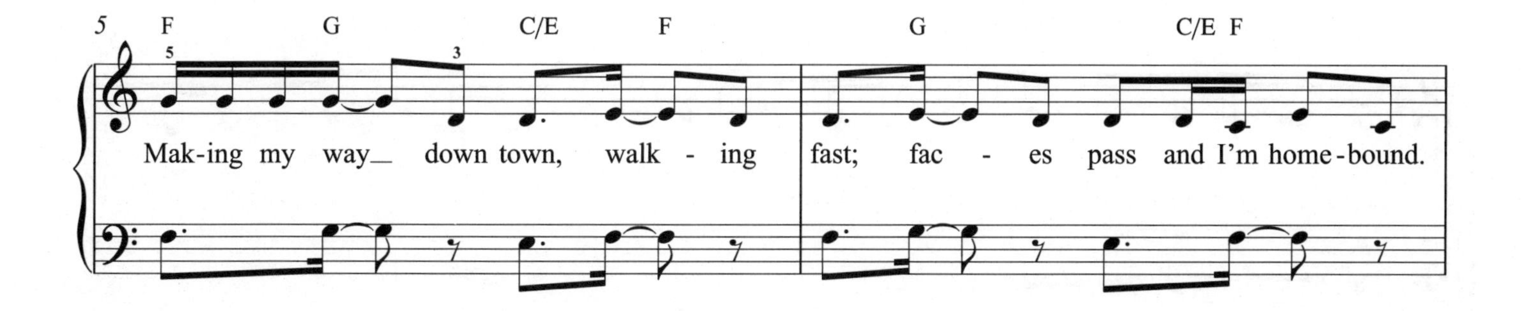

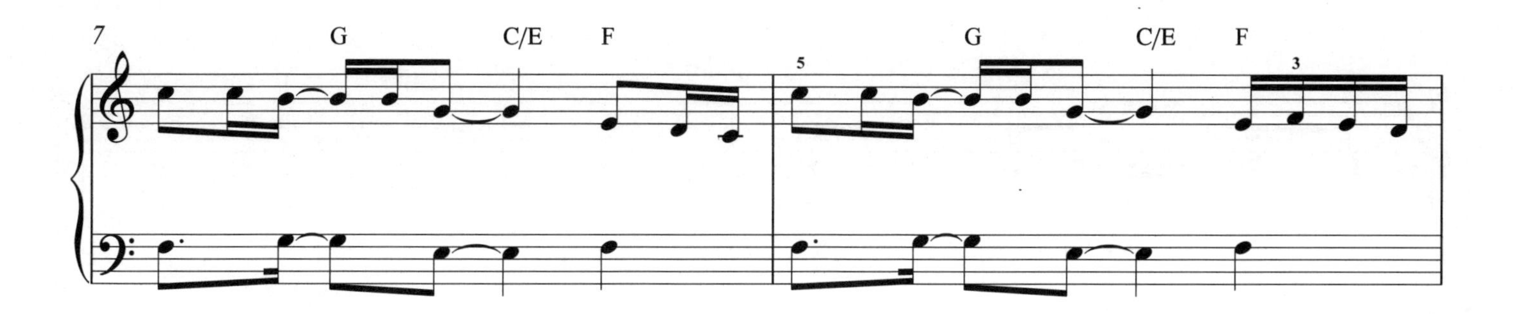

9
G C/E F G C/E F
Star - ing blan - kly a - head, just mak - ing my way, just mak - ing a way through_ the

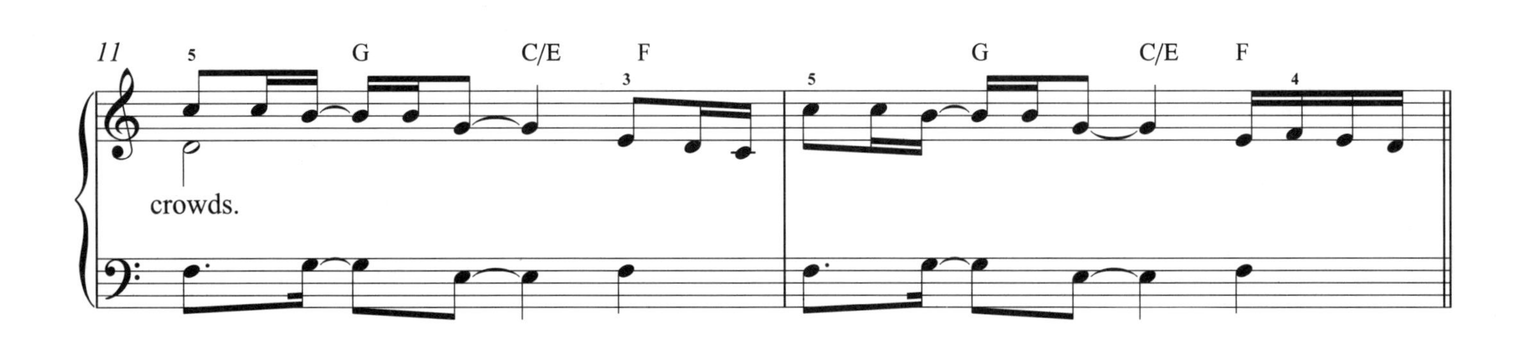
11
G C/E F G C/E F
crowds.

13
F C/G Em F C/G Em
I still need you,_ I still miss you,

15
F C/G Em F G
and now I won - der: If

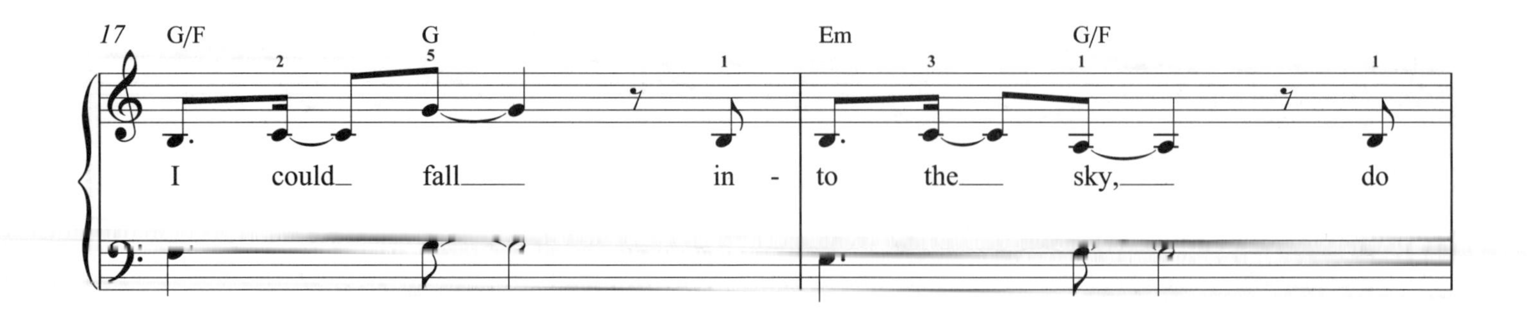
17
G/F G Em G/F
I could_ fall_ in - to the_ sky,_ do

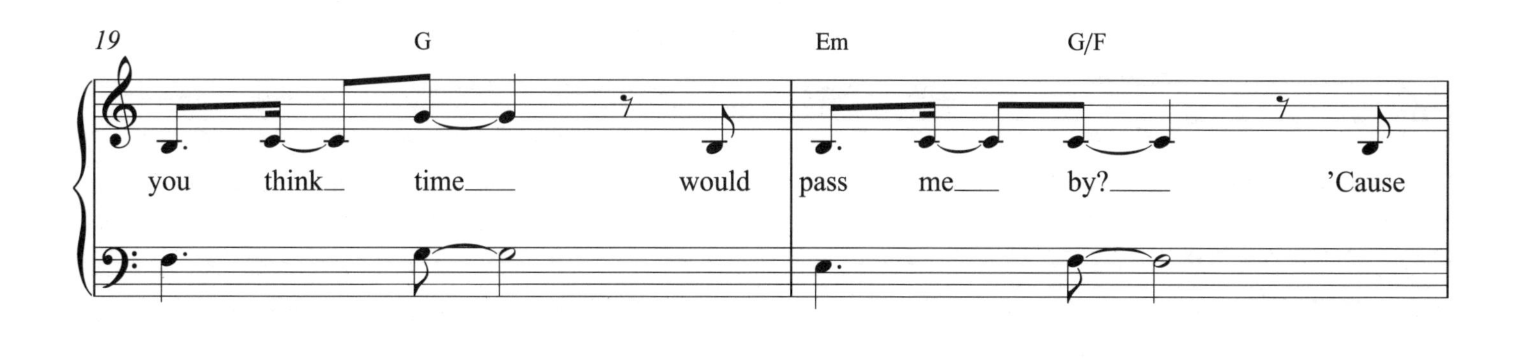
19
G
Em
G/F
you think time would pass me by? 'Cause

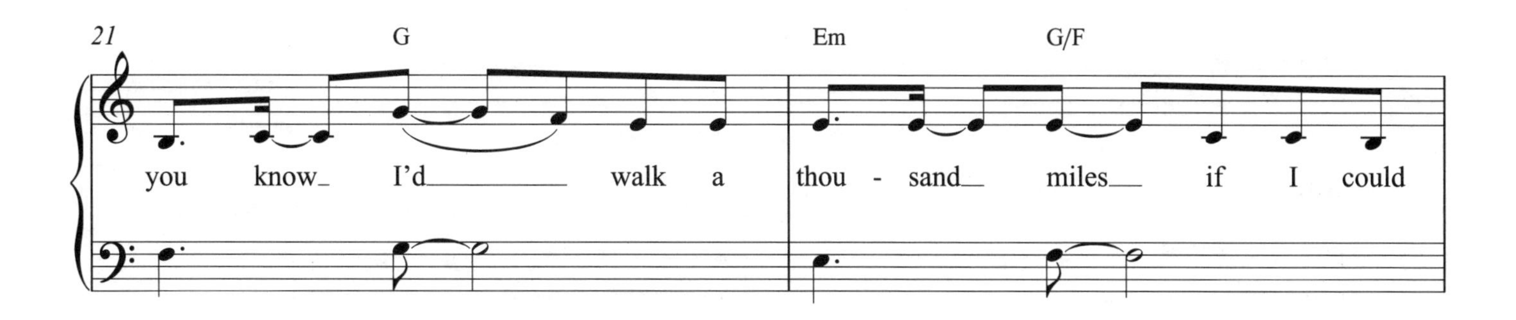
21
G
Em
G/F
you know I'd walk a thou - sand miles if I could

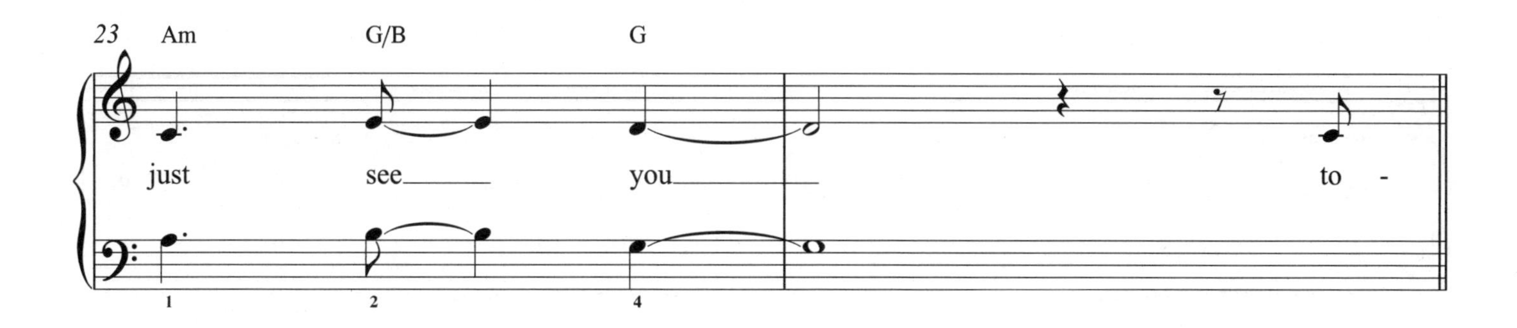
23
Am
G/B
G
just see you to -

25
F
G
C/E
F
G
C/E
F
- night.

27
G
C/E
F
G
C/E
F

Jason Mraz

I'm Yours

Words & Music by Jason Mraz

Jason Mraz performed this relaxed, reggae–based, Grammy-nominated song about giving yourself or your time to someone or something else, in his gigs and it had become a firm crowd favourite, long before he first recorded it on *We Sing, We Dance, We Steal Things*, an album released in 2008 as three separate EPs.

Hints & Tips: Another song with swung quavers and syncopation, practise it slowly and hands separately so that your hands confidently know what they're doing before playing with them together.

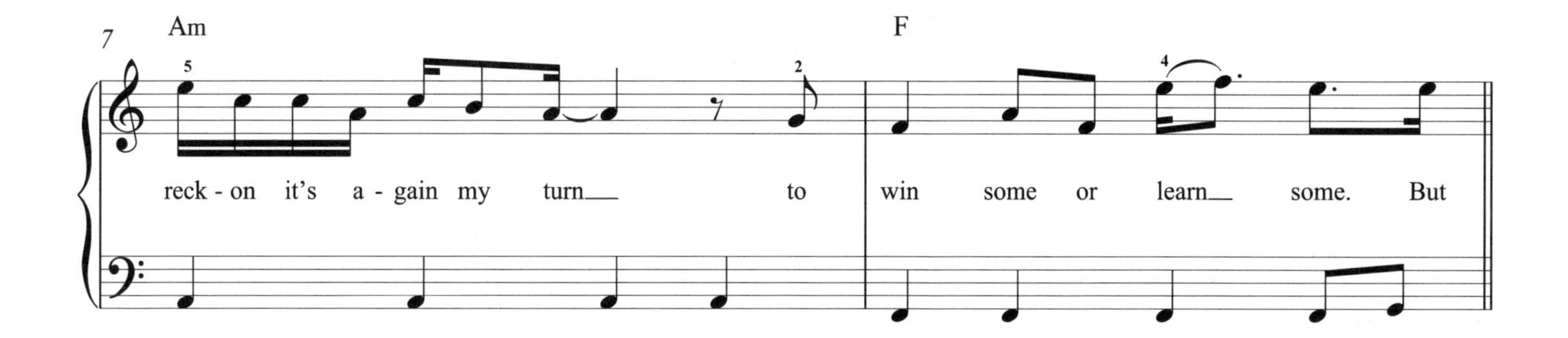
7
Am
F
reck - on it's a - gain my turn to win some or learn some. But

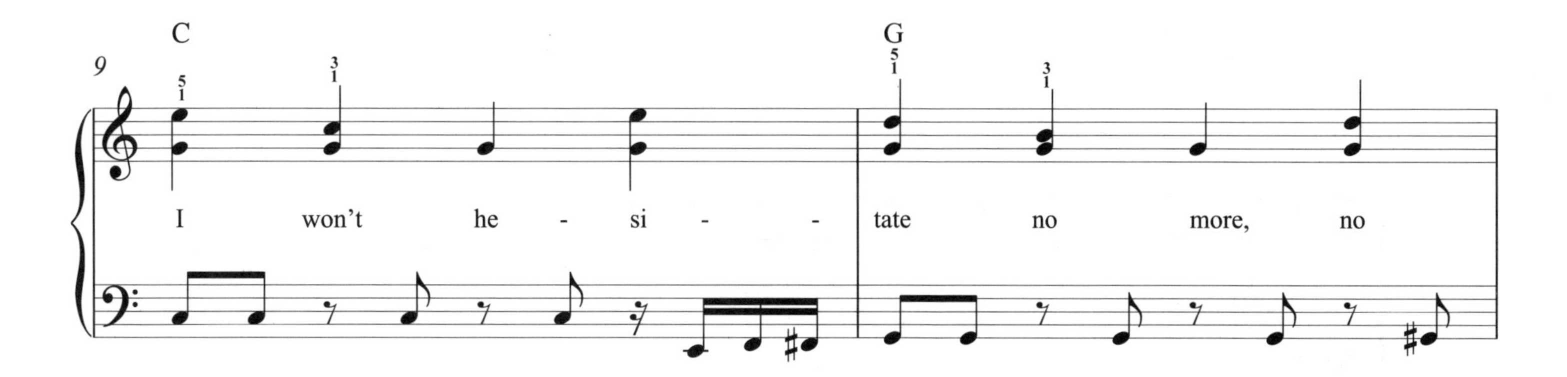
9
C
G
I won't he - si - tate no more, no

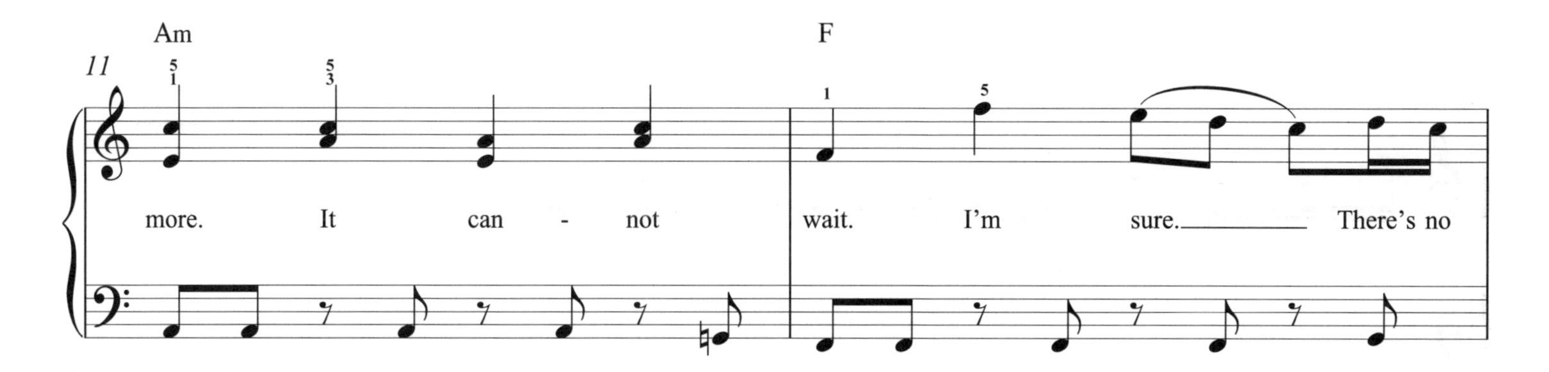
11
Am
F
more. It can - not wait. I'm sure. There's no

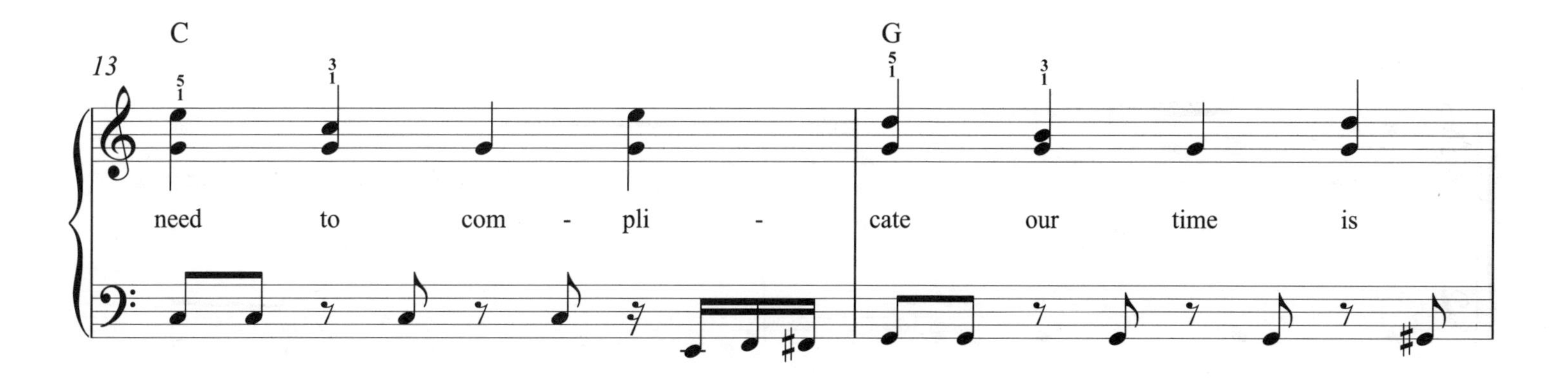
13
C
G
need to com - pli - cate our time is

15
Am
F
C
short this is our fate, I'm yours.

ADELE

Make You Feel My Love

Words & Music by Bob Dylan

Adele's cover of a Bob Dylan song from his 1997 album, *Time Out Of Mind*, was the fifth single taken from her debut album *19*, which entered the UK charts at No. 1 on its release in January 2008. She was the first recipient of the BRIT Awards Critics' Choice, given to artists who, at the time, had yet to release an album.

Hints & Tips: Between bars 17 and 22 take care that the notes sound together and not as if they've been spread.

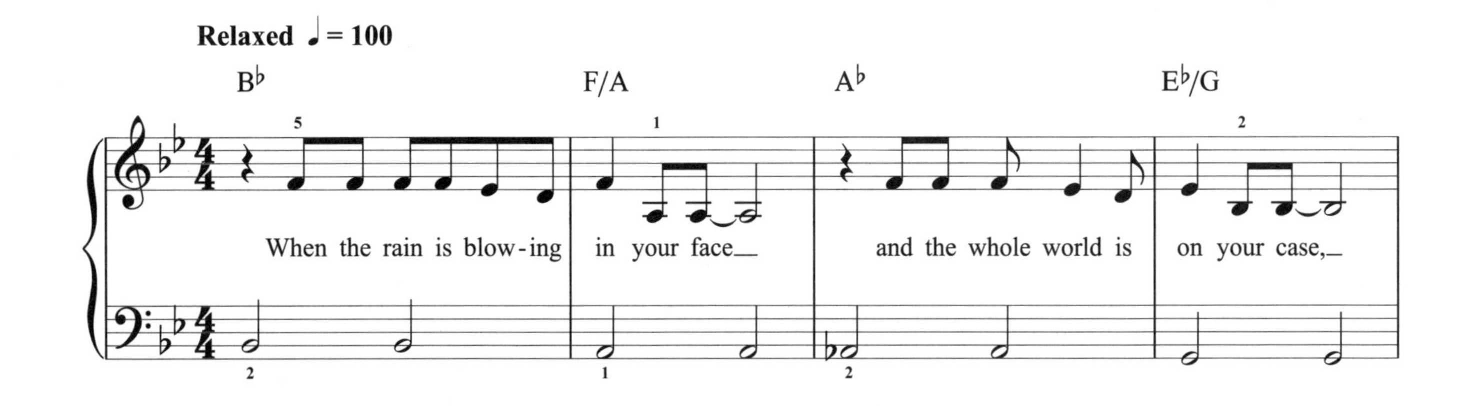

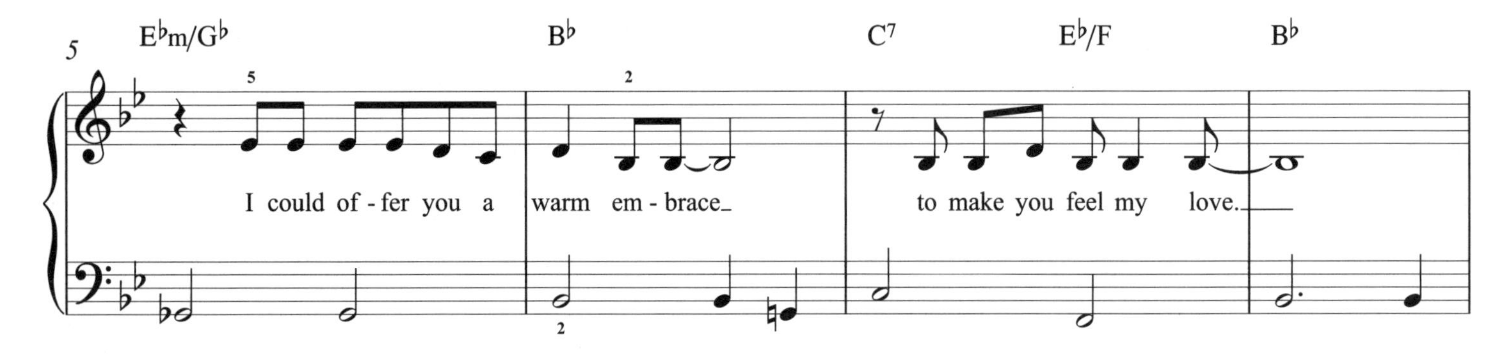

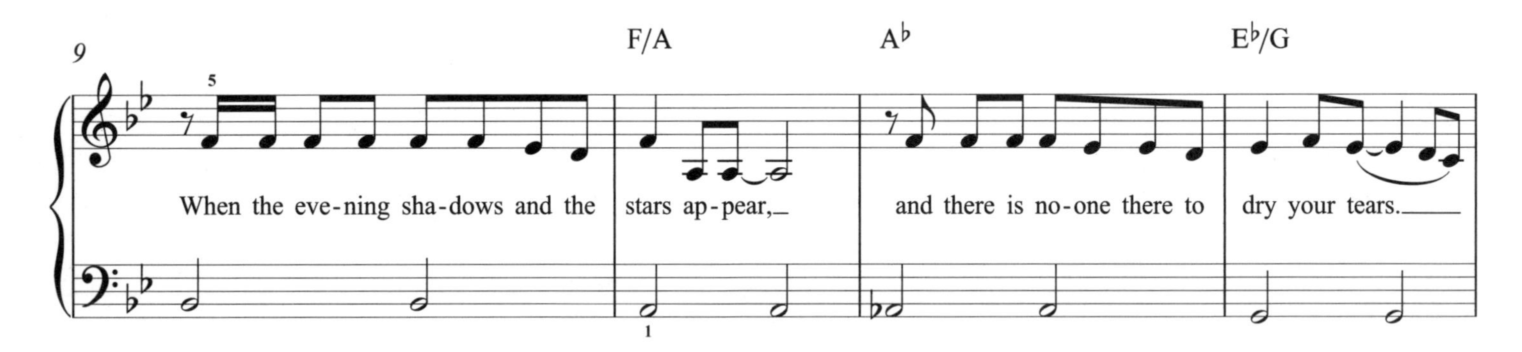

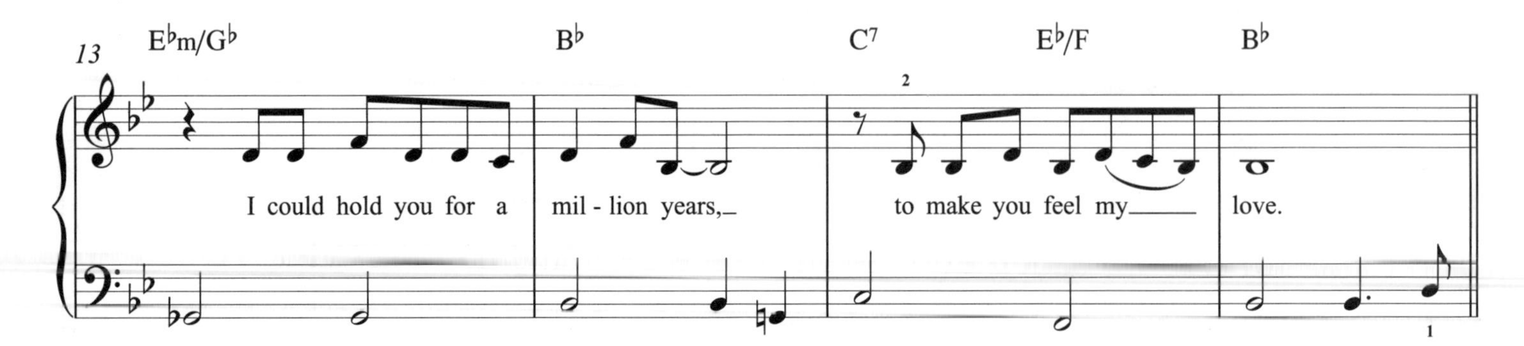

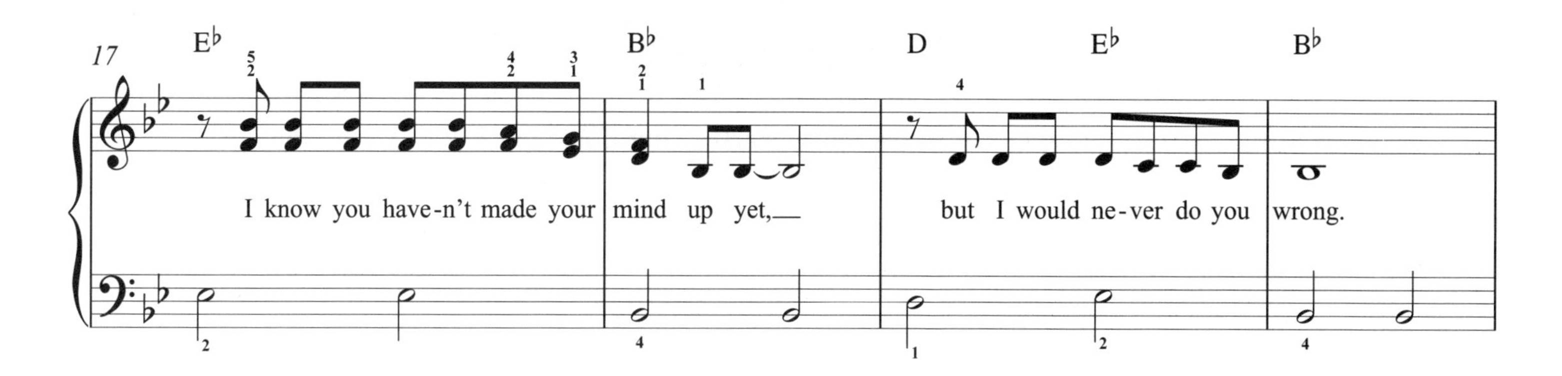
17
E♭ B♭ D E♭ B♭
I know you have-n't made your mind up yet,
but I would ne-ver do you wrong.

21
E♭ B♭ C7
I've known it from the mo-ment that we met,
no doubt in my mind where you be-

24
F B♭ F/A
-long.
I'd go hun-gry, I'd go black and blue.

27
A♭ E♭/G E♭m B♭
I'd go crawl-ing down the a-ven-ue.
No there's no-thing that I would-n't do,

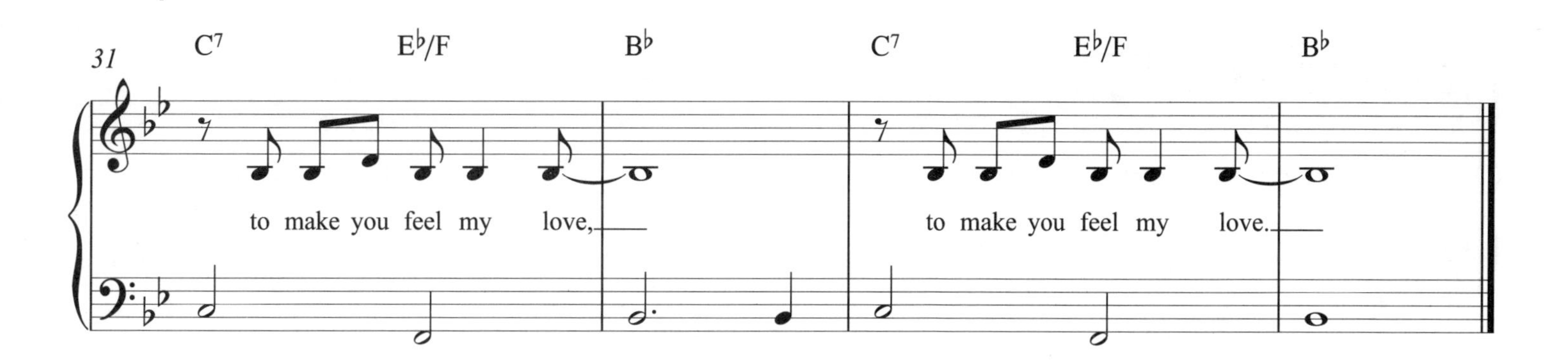
31
C7 E♭/F B♭ C7 E♭/F B♭
to make you feel my love,
to make you feel my love.

Mercy

Words & Music by Duffy & Stephen Booker

With a catchy base-line and summery, jazzy themes, in February 2008 this song became the UK's No. 1 single due to digital downloads alone, three weeks before its physical release. It stayed at No. 1 for five weeks, eventually becoming the year's third best-selling single and receiving nominations for numerous awards.

Hints & Tips: Be careful of the syncopation; practise hands separately paying particular attention to the left hand to lock into the rhythm.

13
Gm7 C G7
2
do but you do it well, I'm un - der your spell.

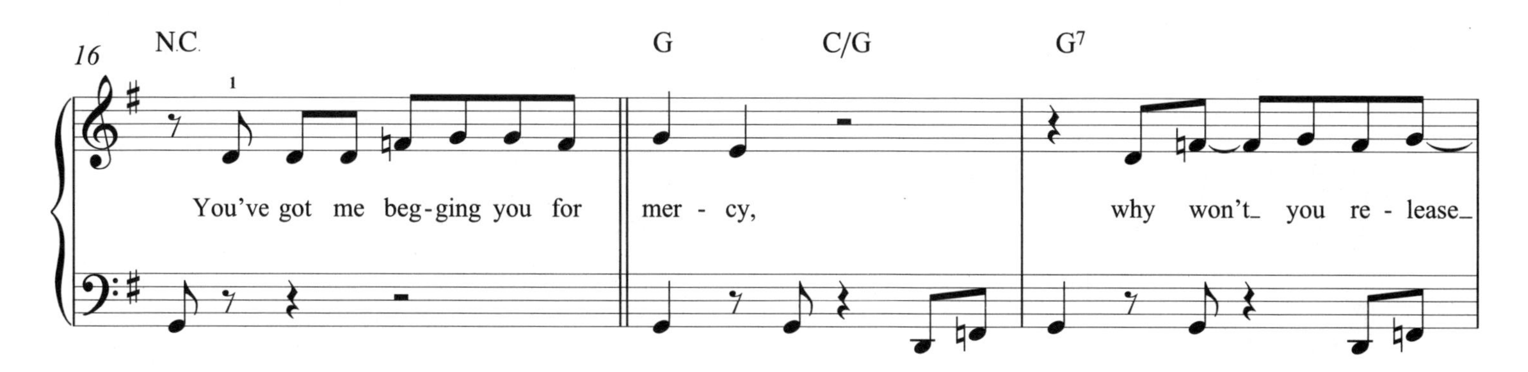
16
N.C. G C/G G7
1
You've got me beg-ging you for mer - cy, why won't you re - lease

19
C/G G7 C/G Gm/C C
2 4 2 3
me? You've got me beg-ging you for mer - cy,

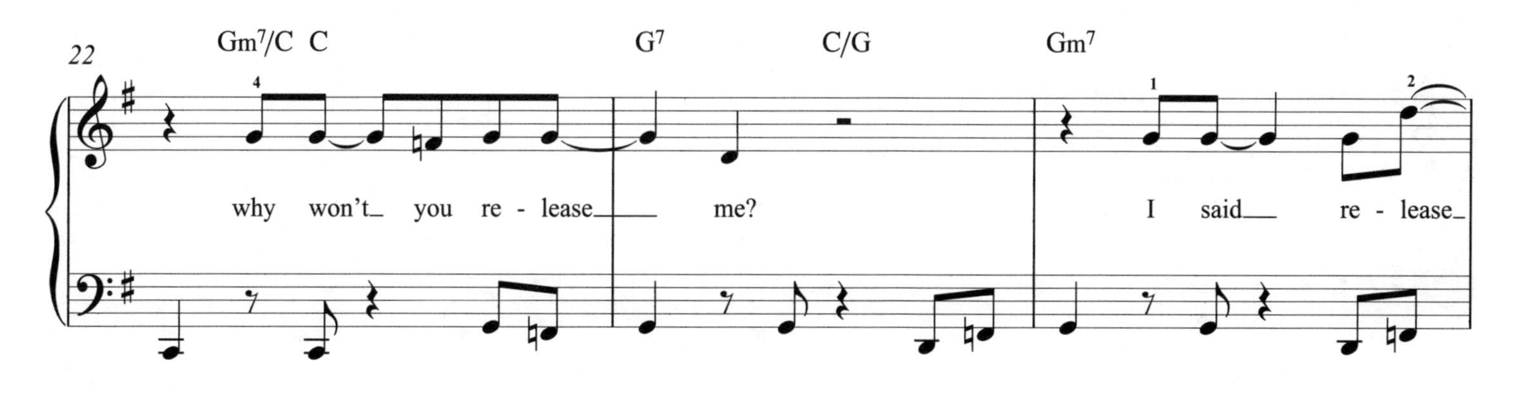
22
Gm7/C C G7 C/G Gm7
4 1 2
why won't you re - lease me? I said re - lease

25
G7/D C7 G
3 2 1
me? Yeah, yeah.

Leona Lewis

A Moment Like This

Words & Music by Jorgen Elofsson & John Reid

Originally recorded by Kelly Clarkson, the first winner of American Idol, Leona Lewis's version of this song was rush-released after she was declared the third winner of the X Factor, debuted at No. 1 in the UK Chart on 24 December 2006, making it the year's coveted Christmas No. 1 single, and stayed there for four weeks.

Hints & Tips: Be ready for the change of key at bar 11, it might sound odd at first, but learn the notes with confidence and it will soon make sense.

9
Cm7
F
G
tell you love has come here and now.
A mo - ment like this.

11
C
G
F
G
Some peo - ple wait a life - time for a mo - ment like this.

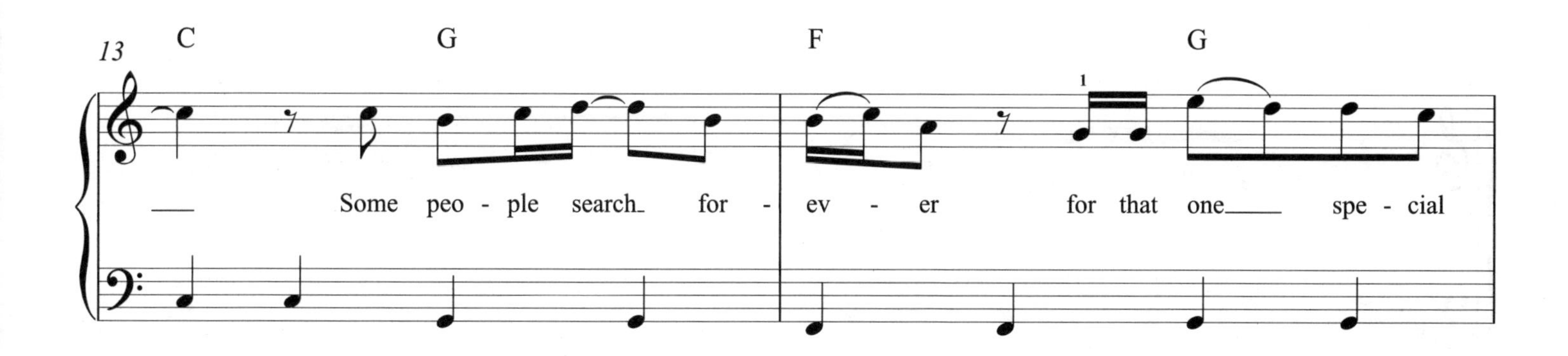
13
C
G
F
G
Some peo - ple search for - ev - er for that one spe - cial

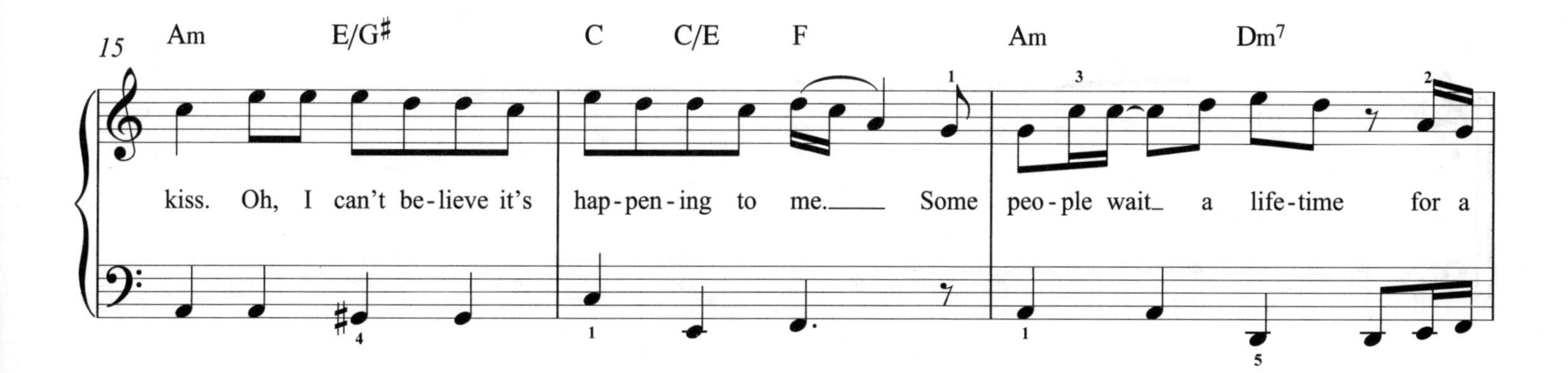
15
Am
E/G♯
C
C/E
F
Am
Dm7
kiss. Oh, I can't be-lieve it's hap-pen-ing to me. Some peo-ple wait a life-time for a

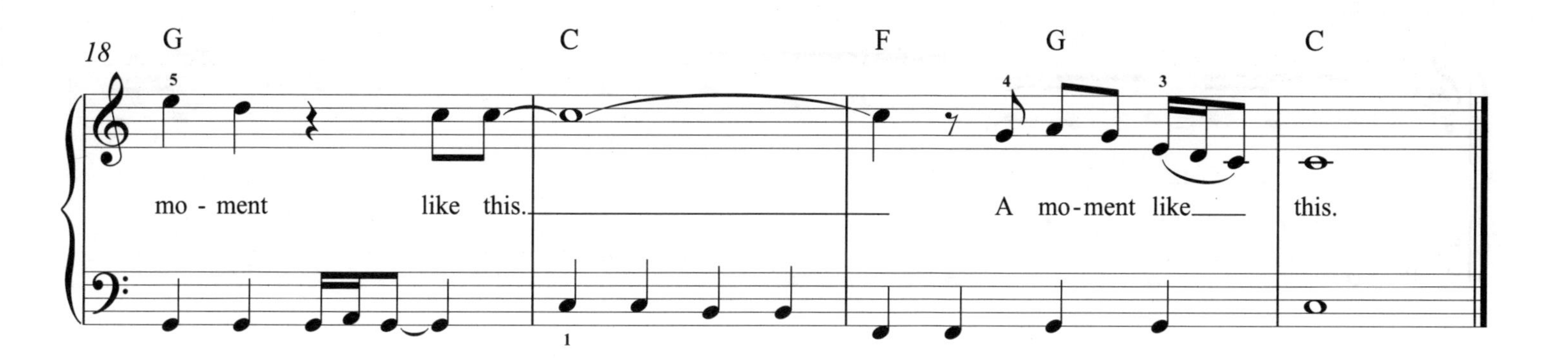
18
G
C
F
G
C
mo - ment like this.
A mo-ment like this.

Take That

Shine

Words & Music by Mark Owen, Gary Barlow, Stephen Robson, Jason Orange & Howard Donald

Taken from their comeback album, *Beautiful World*, this song became Take That's sixth consecutive No. 1 and their tenth overall when it topped the UK charts in March 2007. It won the Ivor Novello award for Most Performed Work in 2007 and the 2008 Brit Award for Best British Single, the band winning Best Live Act.

Hints & Tips: Take care of the repeated notes, making sure they sound even in attack and rhythm.

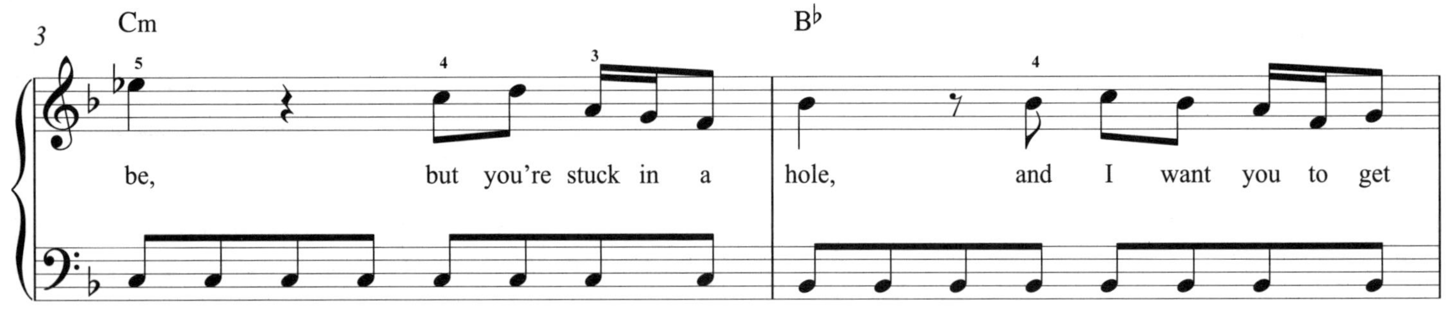

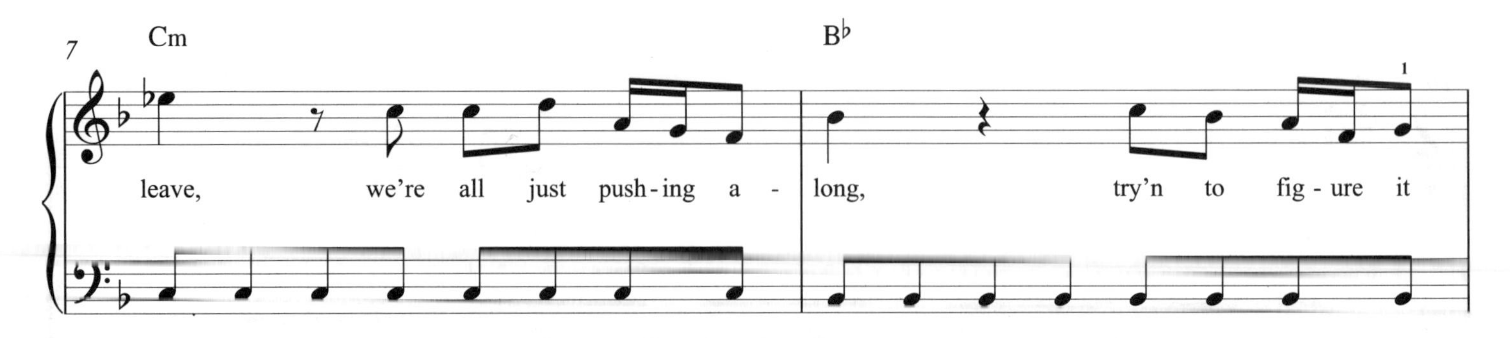

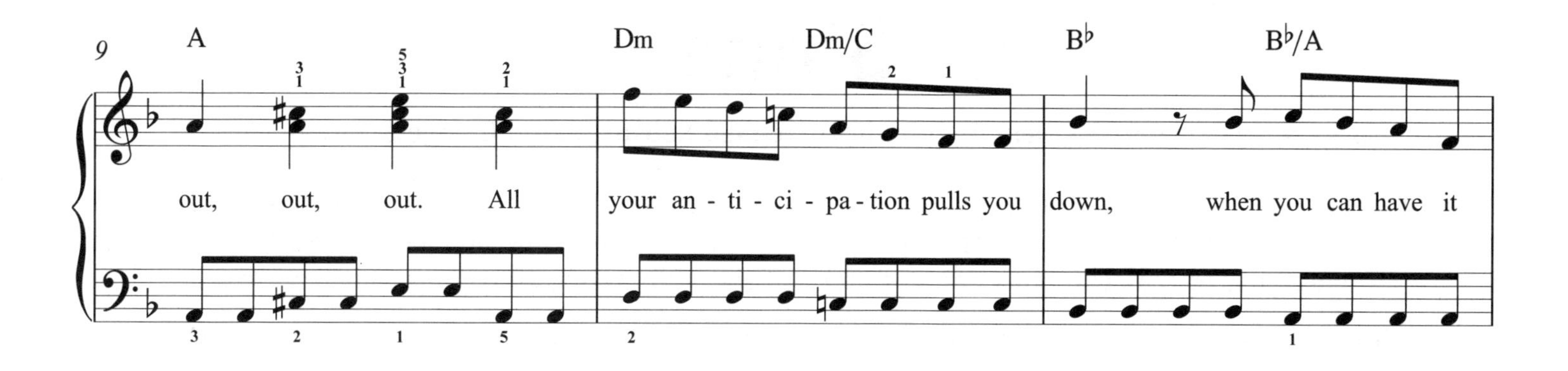
9
A
Dm
Dm/C
B♭
B♭/A
out, out, out. All
your an - ti - ci - pa - tion pulls you
down, when you can have it

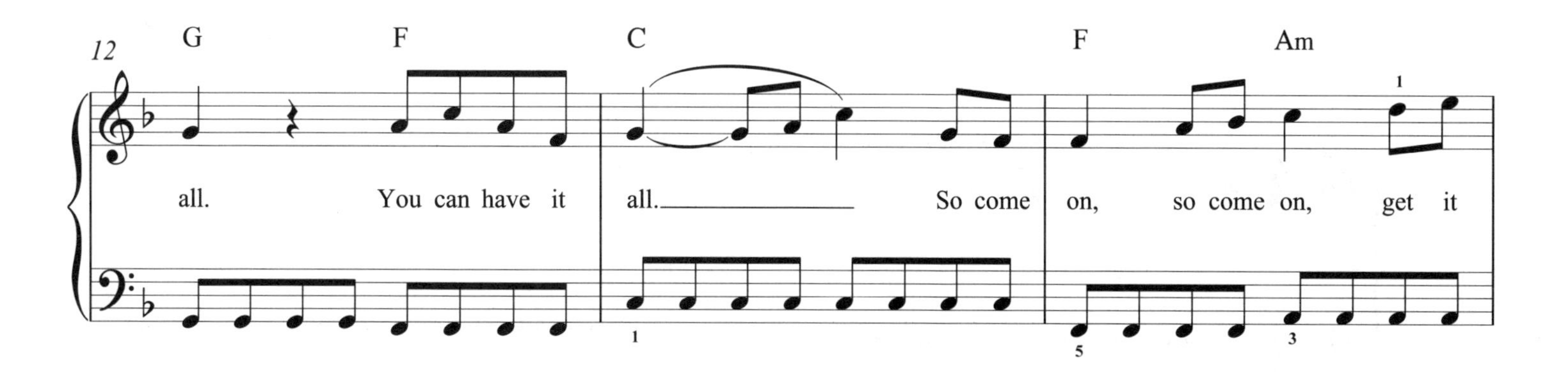
12
G
F
C
F
Am
all. You can have it
all. So come
on, so come on, get it

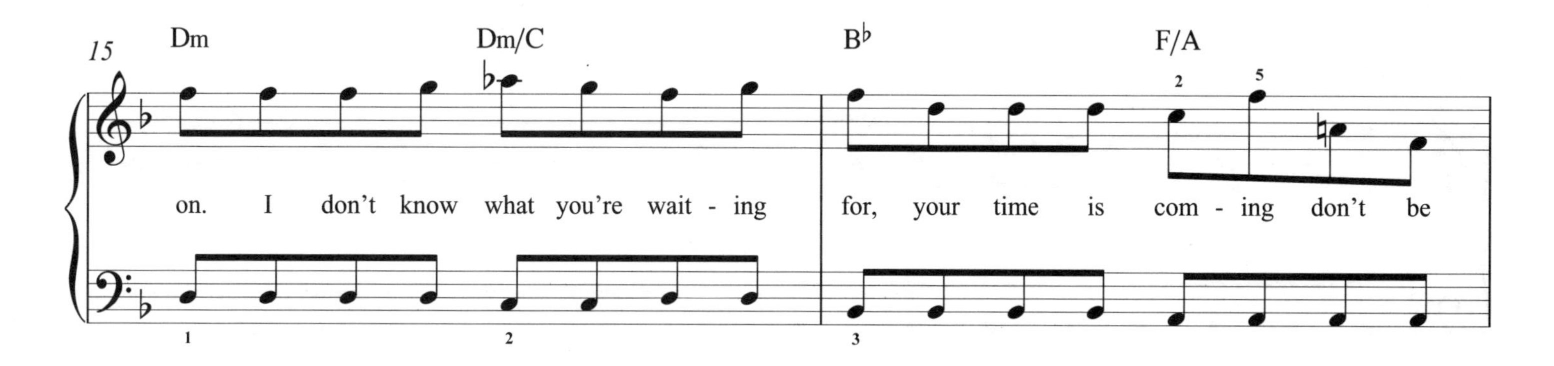
15
Dm
Dm/C
B♭
F/A
on. I don't know what you're wait - ing
for, your time is com - ing don't be

17
G
C
F
Am
Dm
Dm/C
late, hey, hey! So come
on, see the light on your
face, let it shine, just let it

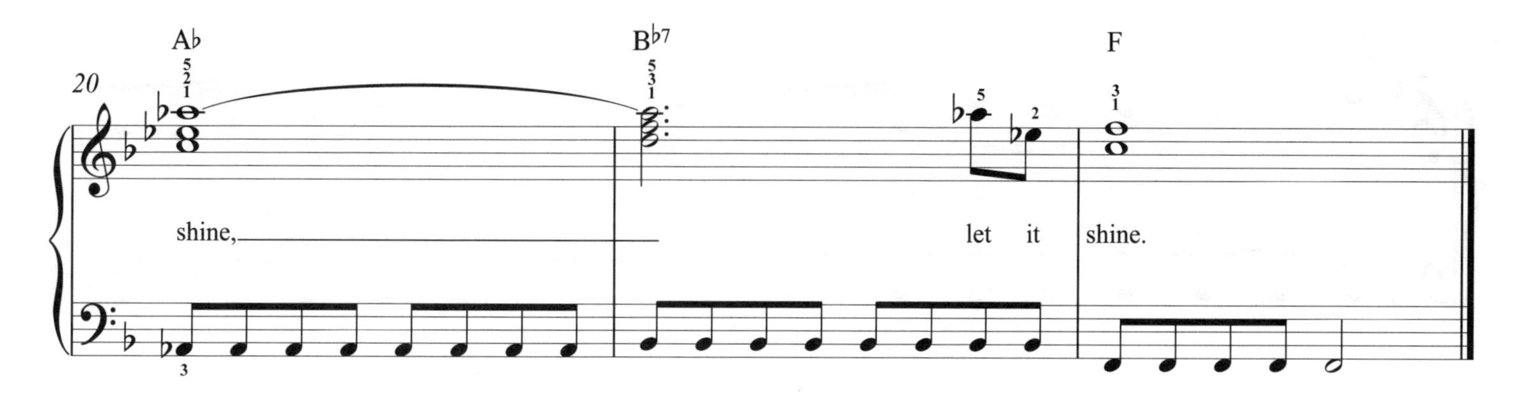
20
A♭
B♭7
F
shine, let it
shine.

Franz Ferdinand

Take Me Out

Words & Music by Alexander Kapranos & Nicholas McCarthy

Taken from their 2004 Mercury Prize winning debut album, this Indie anthem was the breakthrough hit for the Scottish band who named themselves after the Austrian Archduke whose assassination triggered the outbreak of World War I, after watching racehorse Archduke Ferdinand win the 2001 Northumberland Plate.

Hints & Tips: You might find the metronome marking a little too fast when you reach the repeated notes in bar 4, so practise slowly aiming to play rhythmically rather than fast.

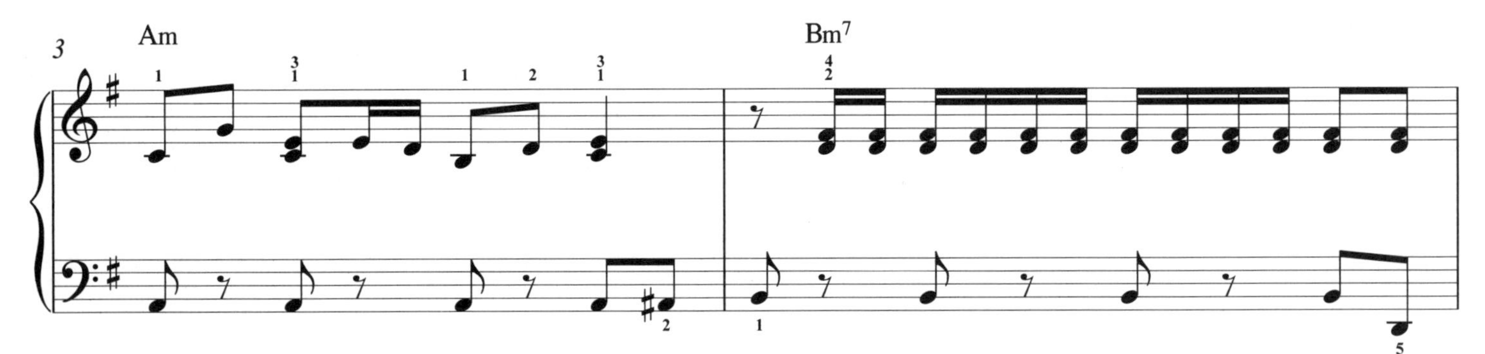

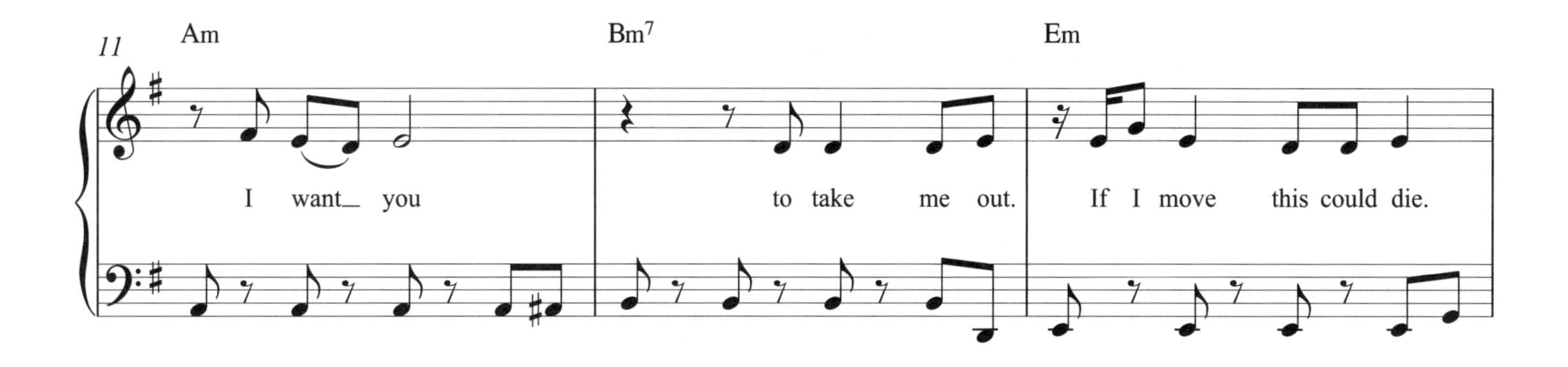
11
Am
Bm7
Em
I want_ you
to take me out.
If I move this could die.

14
Am
Bm7
N.C.
If eyes move this could die.
Come on,
take me out.

17
Em
Am

20
Bm7
Em

22

JAMES MORRISON

You Give Me Something

Words & Music by James Morrison & Eg White

Morrison became the best-selling male solo artist of 2006 in the UK after *Undiscovered*, a collection of raw, bittersweet, bluesy, folk-soul songs and his first album, debuted at the top of the UK Albums Chart and sold more than one million copies worldwide, no doubt assisted by the popularity of this song, his first single.

Hints & Tips: Several of the phrases in this song have a wide melodic range. Once you have got to grips with the fingering and can play both the melody and accompaniment smoothly, give each phrase a sense of line by introducing some dynamics.

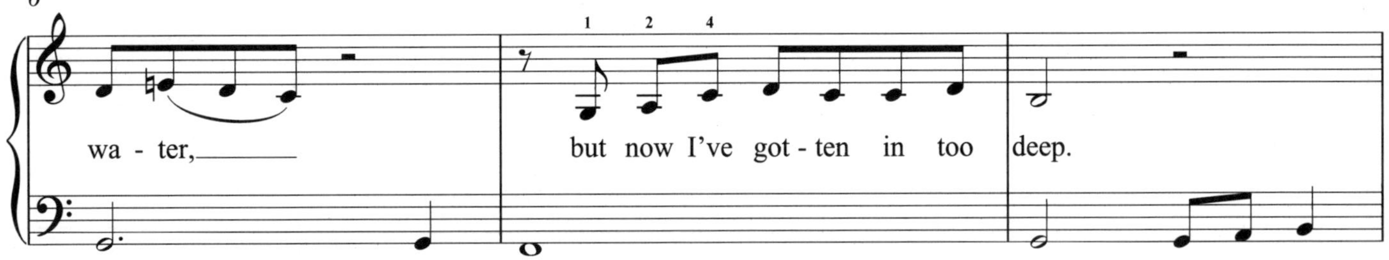

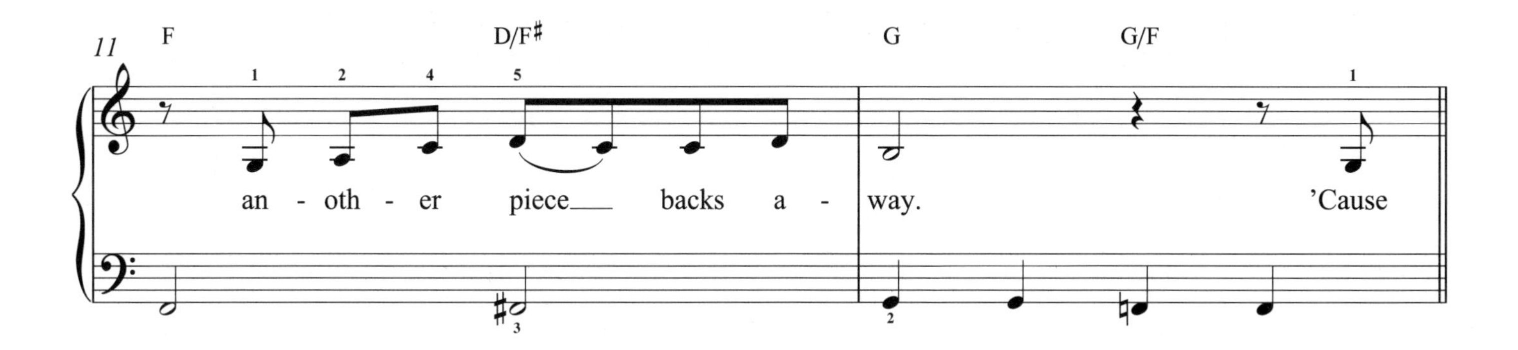
11
F D/F♯ G G/F
an - oth - er piece backs a - way. 'Cause

13
Em Am Dm G Em Am
you give me some - thing that makes me scared al - right. This could be

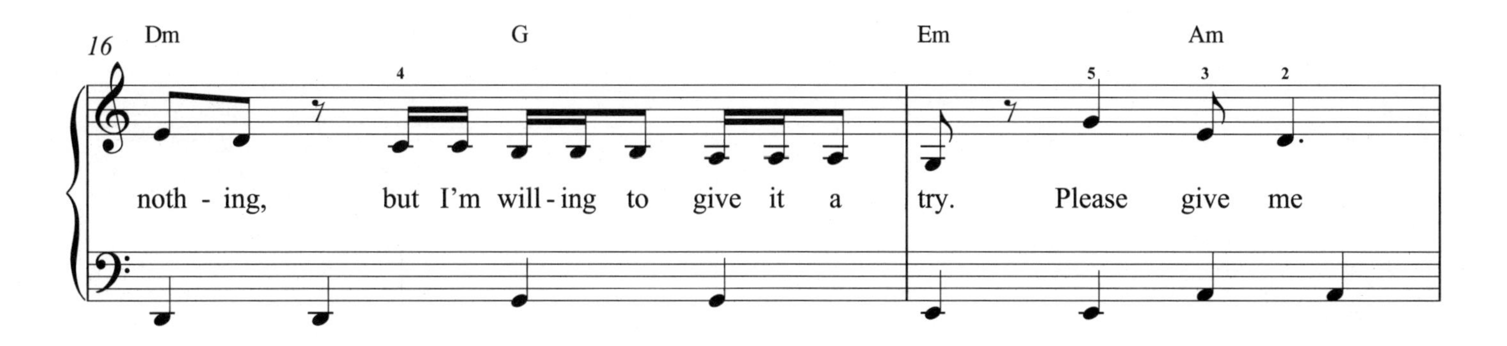
16
Dm G Em Am
noth - ing, but I'm will - ing to give it a try. Please give me

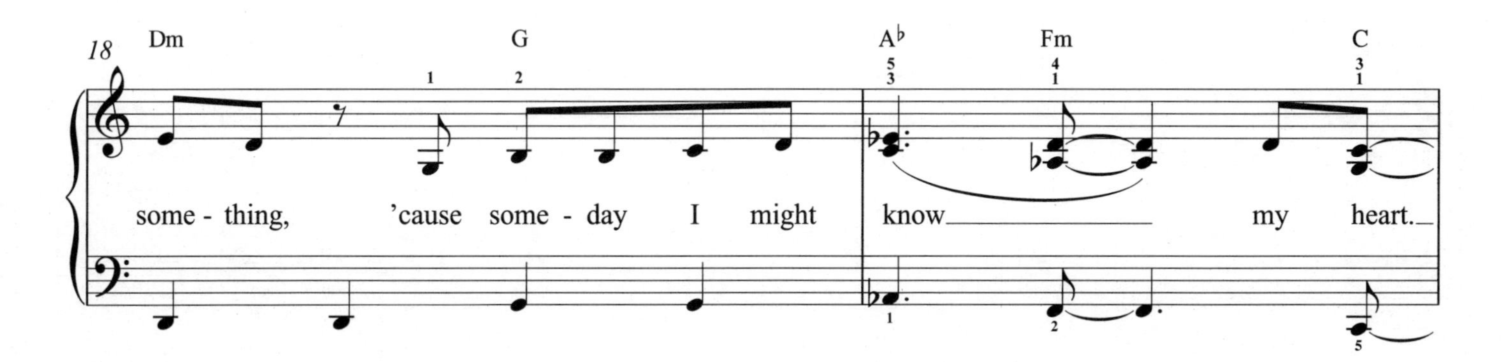
18
Dm G A♭ Fm C
some - thing, 'cause some - day I might know my heart.

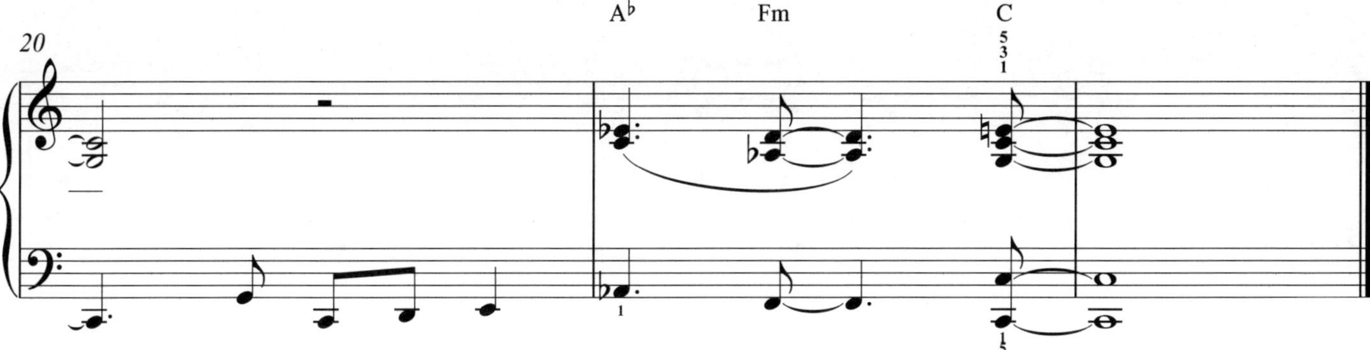
20
A♭ Fm C

Westlife

You Raise Me Up

Words & Music by Brendan Graham & Rolf Løvland

Only The Beatles, Elvis and Cliff Richard have had more No. 1 hit singles than Westlife's 18. In November 2005, after a gap of two years, this song, originally an instrumental, 'Silent Story', recorded by Secret Garden on their album *Once In A Red Moon*, became their 13th and went on to become the UK Record of the Year.

Hints & Tips: Listen carefully to ensure you are playing both notes in the left-hand chords at exactly the same time. This will create a steady and simple background to the elegant right-hand melody which you should play as legato (smoothly) as possible.

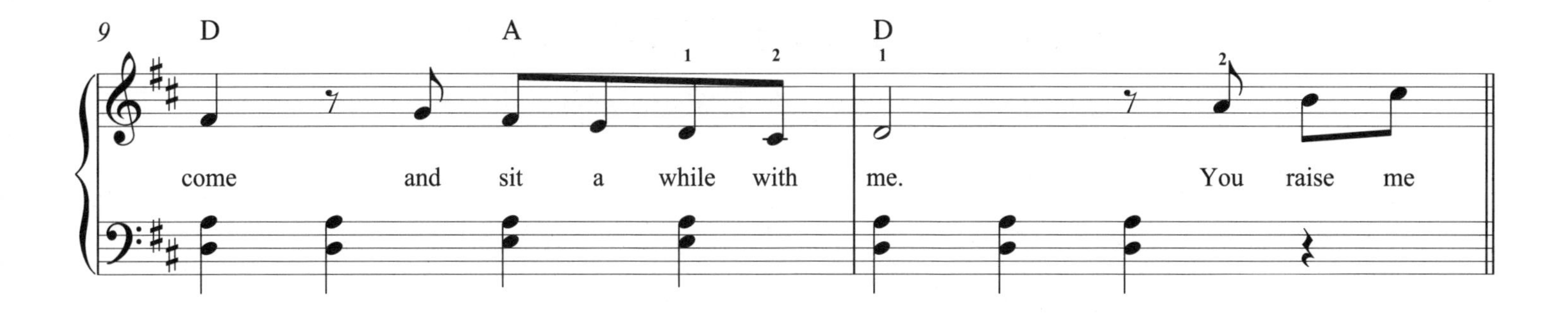
9
D A D
come and sit a while with me. You raise me

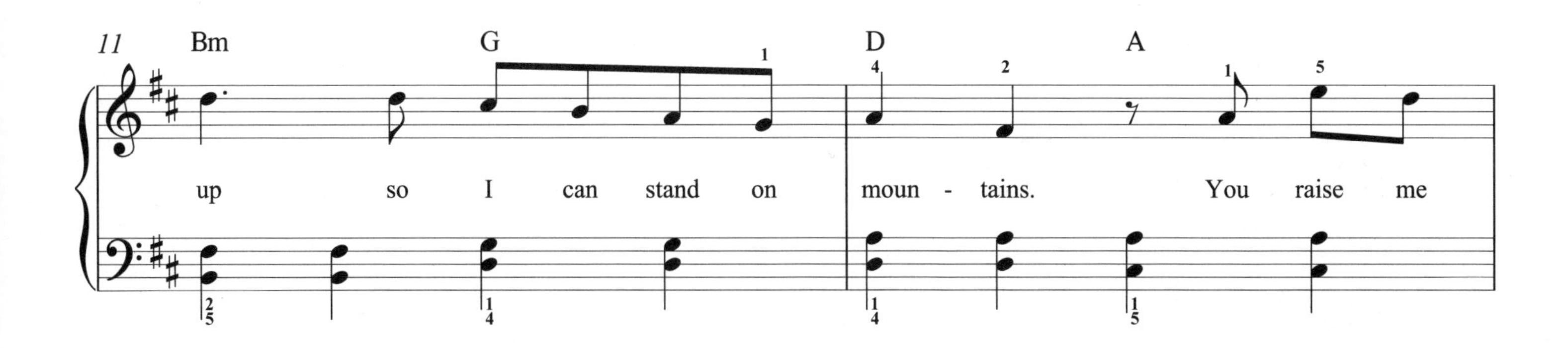
11
Bm G D A
up so I can stand on moun - tains. You raise me

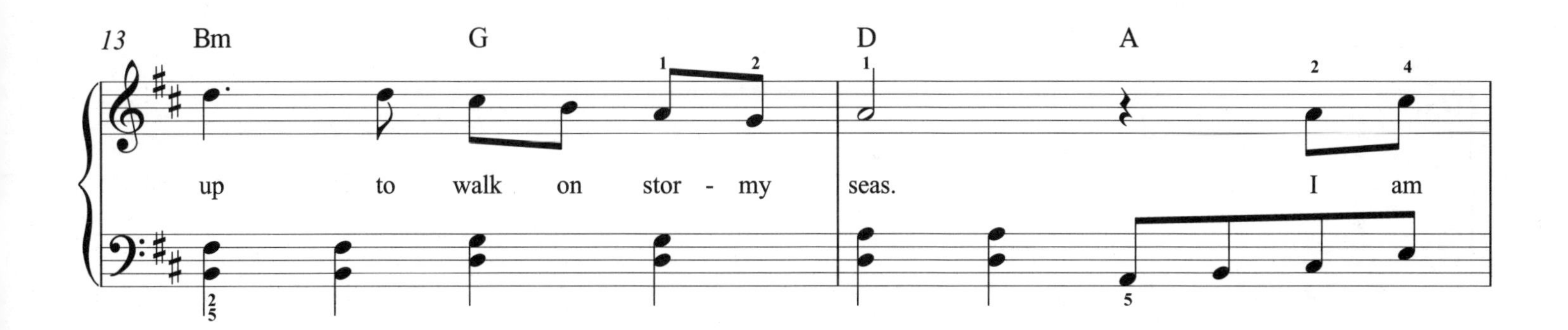
13
Bm G D A
up to walk on stor - my seas. I am

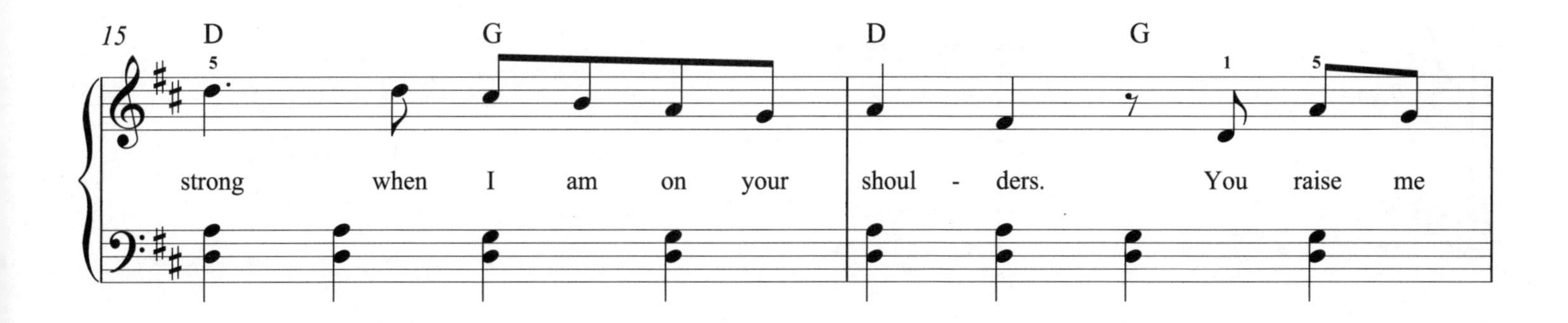
15
D G D G
strong when I am on your shoul - ders. You raise me

17
D A D
up to more than I can be.

RIHANNA FEAT. JAY-Z

Umbrella

Words & Music by Terius Nash, Christopher Stewart, Thaddis Harrell & Shawn Carter

This single was 2007's biggest seller on the United World Chart, spending seven weeks at No. 1 on the USA's Billboard Hot 100 and topping the UK Chart for ten consecutive weeks, the longest reign since Wet Wet Wet in 1994, and ironically at a time when the country was beset by extreme rainfall and flooding.

Hints & Tips: Although this piece is fairly straightforward, do practise it slowly at first, ensuring that the notes in the right hand and left hand sound at exactly the same time when they are supposed to—most of the time!

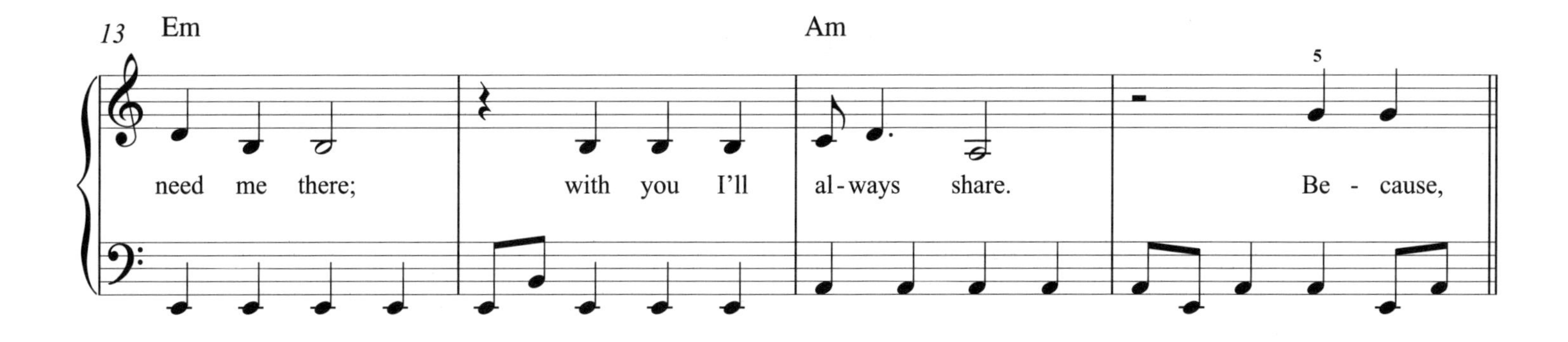
13
Em
Am
5
need me there;
with you I'll
al-ways share.
Be - cause,

17
F
C
when the sun
shines we'll shine to-geth -
er, told you
I'll be here for-ev -
5

21
G
Am
3 1
- er, said I'll
al - ways be your friend,
took an oath I'm - a

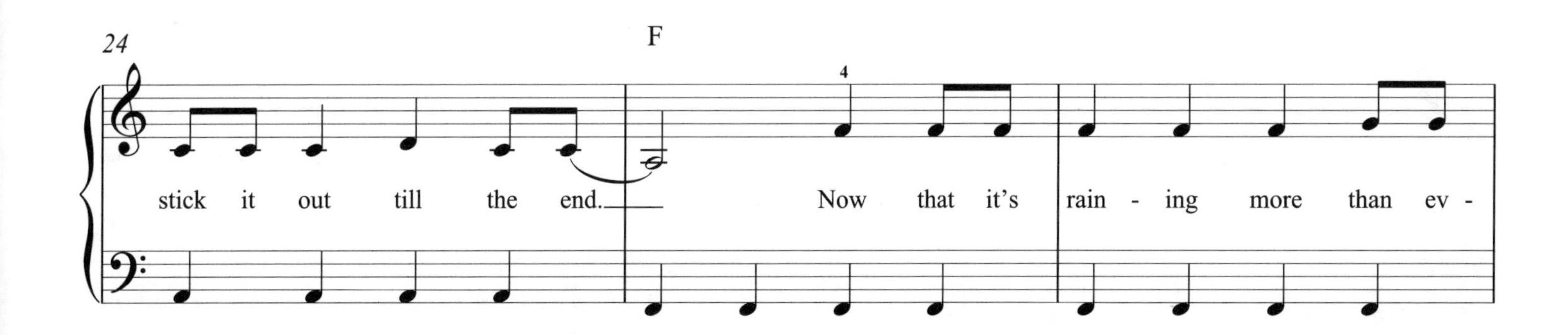
24
F
4
stick it out till the end.
Now that it's
rain - ing more than ev -

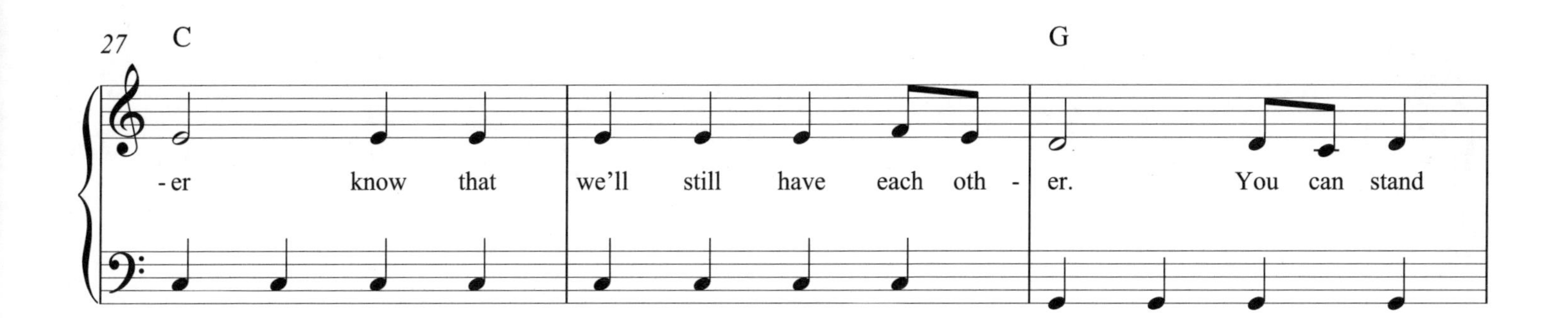
27
C
G
- er know that
we'll still have each oth -
er. You can stand

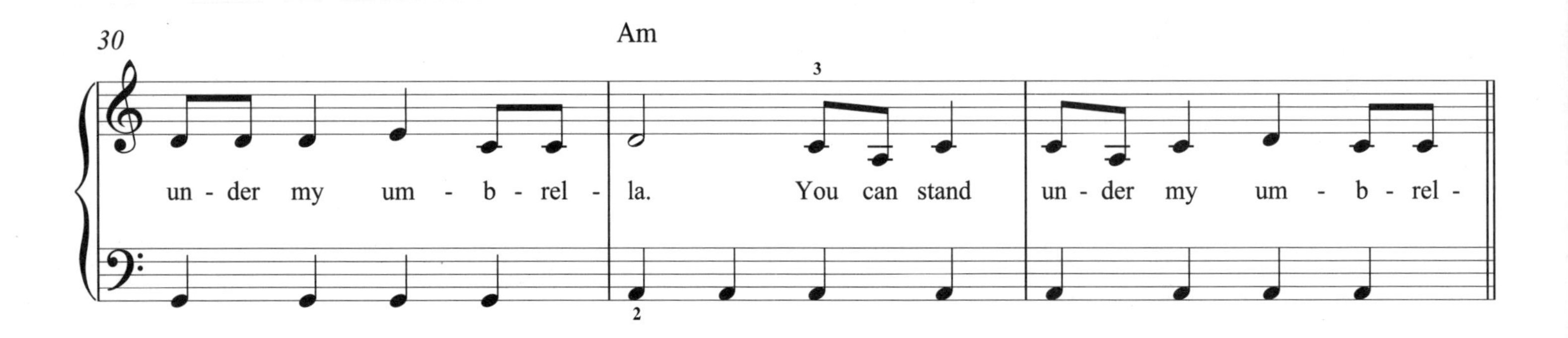
30
Am
3
un - der my um - b - rel - la. You can stand un - der my um - b - rel -
2

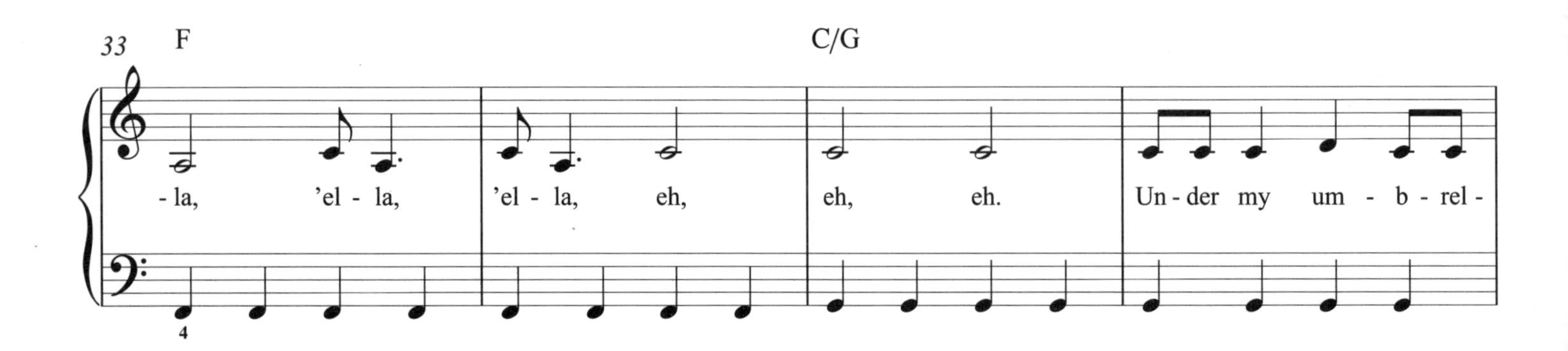
33
F
C/G
- la, 'el - la, 'el - la, eh, eh, eh. Un - der my um - b - rel -
4

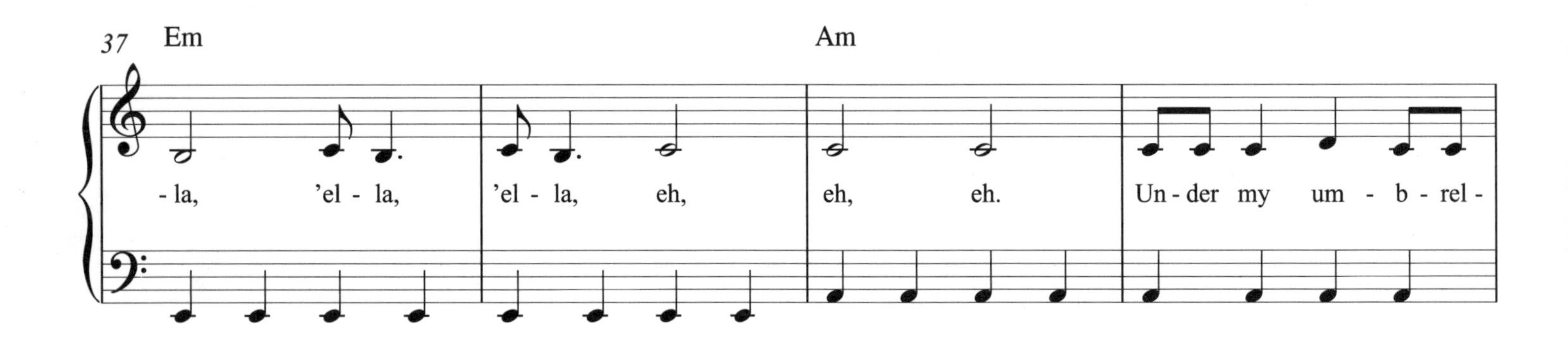
37
Em
Am
- la, 'el - la, 'el - la, eh, eh, eh. Un - der my um - b - rel -

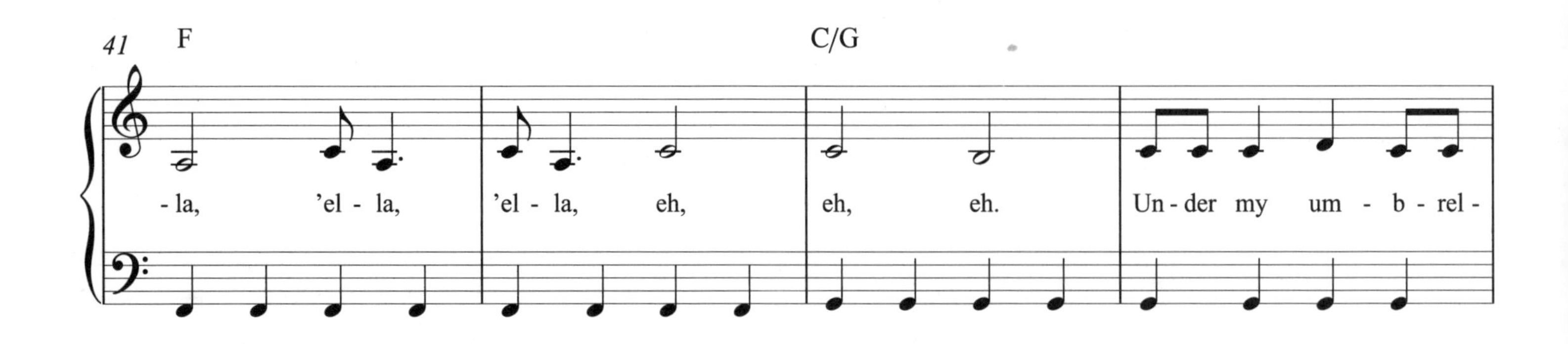
41
F
C/G
- la, 'el - la, 'el - la, eh, eh, eh. Un - der my um - b - rel -

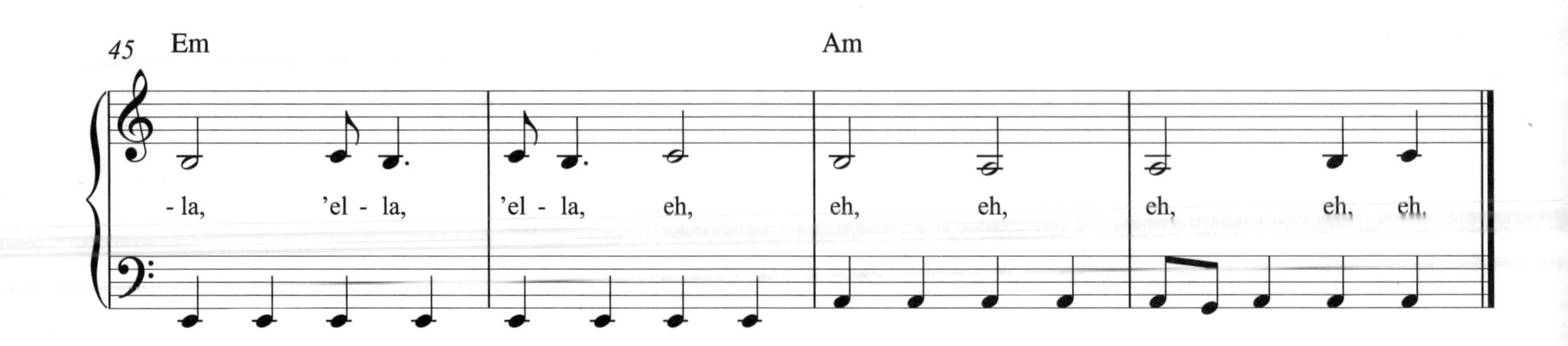
45
Em
Am
- la, 'el - la, 'el - la, eh, eh, eh, eh, eh, eh.

1 2 3 4 5 6 7 8 9